An
Auctioneer's
Lot

Also by Richard Harton from Macdonald

UNDER THE HAMMER

An Auctioneer's Lot

RICHARD HARTON

Macdonald

A *Sphere* Book

First published in Great Britain in 1992 by
Macdonald & Co (Publishers) Ltd
London & Sydney

Photoset in North Wales by
Derek Doyle & Associates, Mold, Clwyd
Printed and bound in Great Britain by
BPCC Hazells Ltd
Member of BPCC Ltd

A CIP catalogue record for this book is available
from the British Library

ISBN 0 356 19753 0

Macdonald & Co (Publishers) Ltd
165 Great Dover Street
London SE1 4YA

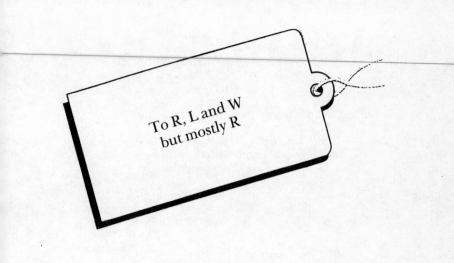

To R, L and W
but mostly R

Chapter 1

'Good morning, I'm Richard . . .'

'I know who you are,' she snarled. 'You're working for *him*, aren't you?'

'I have been retained by Mr Dennison to . . .'

'That swine!' she howled, clenching her fists and stamping her foot in an overt display of impotent fury. 'That swine! How *dare* he?'

It didn't seem to me that Mr Dennison was daring much at all. For one thing, it was me, not him, standing on the doorstep of his estranged wife's Chelsea home. If anyone was being daring it was me, and that was seriously out of character since I generally tried to avoid acts of conspicuous heroism.

'How *dare* he?' she repeated, somehow injecting even more venom into the rhetorical enquiry than she had at the first time of asking. 'The *swine*!'

'Mrs Dennison . . .'

'Don't you "Mrs Dennison" me, you . . . you vulture!'

'Mrs Dennison,' I continued, patiently but firmly, 'I don't think that's going to get us anywhere.'

'Don't you lecture me! How *dare* you!'

That was more like it. At least I was getting some credit for my foolhardy gallantry.

'I have been instructed by Mr Dennison's solicitors . . .'

'More vultures! Ugh! You all make me sick! Do you hear me, you ghastly man? You make me physically sick!'

1

It crossed my mind that in her present highly excited state she might just *be* physically sick at any moment. I stood my ground, however. Any sign of weakness now would probably result in my throat being torn out on the spot.

' . . . and they assured me,' I went on, quietly, 'that you had agreed the appointment and . . .'

'I agreed nothing!' she snapped, glaring imperiously down her long, aristocratic nose at what she obviously believed to be a member of a sub-species.'

' . . . And that it was your intention to co-operate in the . . .'

'Co-operate! Ha! Me! Co-operate with anything that slug has arranged? Don't be absurd!'

' . . . to co-operate in the valuation of the contents of this house.'

'Never!' she said. 'Never!'

'In that case I won't waste any more of my time, Madam,' I replied. 'I'll simply do the valuation the easy way. Good morning.'

'The easy way?' she said, as I turned to go. 'What do you mean – the easy way?'

She was hooked. The question now was whether or not I could reel her in.

'I'll simply work from Mr Dennison's inventory,' I said, pausing on the bottom step.

'Inventory? What inventory? I know nothing of an inventory.'

'Well, he has one,' I assured her, 'and I shall just value the contents on the basis of the inventory descriptions. Good morning, Mrs Dennison.'

'Wait!'

She was just inches away from the landing net now.

'Yes?'

'How can you value things properly like that? You wouldn't be able to tell whether they were genuine or not.'

2

'No, I agree. I would have to take Mr Dennison's word for that. Of course, he assures me all the main pieces are absolutely right.'

'Poppycock!' she exploded. 'That Philistine couldn't tell a Gauguin from a grandfather clock.'

'Well, that was the whole idea of my attending at the house,' I said, 'but since you would prefer me not to make the valuation that way . . .'

Her face contorted as the number of noughts on the divorce settlement flashed before her eyes. 'Oh, I suppose you'd better come in,' she said.

Plop! Safely in the net.

I felt I had every right to feel a little smug. It was the fourth attempt that had been made by various valuers to get into the Dennison marital love-nest, and I was the first to meet with success. Since it was also my first assignment as manager of the valuations office of Hampson & Company Limited, I was particularly pleased to have overcome the embittered lady's rebuffs. Not that getting inside the door was any reason to drop my guard. On the contrary, the tiger's den is no place to relax.

'Wait here,' Hermione Dennison ordered as soon as she'd closed the door. 'Don't move!'

She strode, purposefully, down the long hallway, a strange, tall, severe-looking figure with her straight black hair, and dark, shapeless clothing. I'd been advised by an exasperated solicitor that she was artistic, volatile and had no sense of humour. I hadn't seen anything yet to give me cause to contradict him.

I stood, rooted to the spot just inside the door, awaiting her return and trying to gauge what sort of a job it would be. If the entrance hall was anything to go by, it was going to prove quite interesting. The Dennisons looked to possess some very nice things.

Moments later, the châtelaine of number Forty-One, Plymouth Street, returned with a companion.

3

'This is the thing I spoke of, Molly,' Mrs Dennison said, pointing a disdainful finger at me, 'don't let it out of your sight!'

Molly studied me intently, noting and mentally filing away all distinguishing characteristics as though she thought she might have to pick me out in a police identity parade at a later date. I'm ashamed to say that I in turn studied Molly. Next to her tall, angular mistress, the cruel joke of a body that nature had given her was emphasised and underlined. Physically, she was a female cross between Quilp and Quasimodo: her tiny frame bent almost double, her spine twisted into an obscene hump over her left shoulder.

'Aye, Mu'm,' she replied, in a thick Glaswegian accent, 'I'll no tak' ma eyes off him.'

Hermione Dennison nodded, gave me a last, long, contemptuous look and began to ascend the stairs to the next floor.

As she disappeared around the bend in the staircase, I turned to Molly. 'Good morning,' I said, 'I'm Richard Harton.'

She nodded, but made no reply.

'I usually start my valuations on the top floor,' I went on, 'but under the circumstances, perhaps it would be as well if we began in here today.' I gestured to the closed door on my left.

Molly nodded again.

I walked over to the door, opened it and entered a spacious, well furnished drawing room. Molly followed hard on my heels. She was obviously going to follow her mistress's instructions to the letter.

I put down my briefcase and took out my notebook and pen. As I looked around the room I saw that Molly was standing with the door just ajar. Rather than observing me, she appeared to be listening intently to what was going on elsewhere. After a moment she gently and quietly closed the door.

4

'She's awa' t' her bed,' she announced, with a broad smile. 'She'll be having another o' her migraines. We'll no see anymore o' her this morning.'

'I can't say I'm wildly upset about that,' I ventured, hoping that Molly was indeed the double agent she suddenly appeared to be.

'Aye, she's a very difficult woman,' she replied, without hesitating. 'It took her twelve years to drive hi'self awa' but she did it in the end.'

I smiled. 'You think he was right to go, then?' I asked.

'No, Mr Harton, I dinn'a say that. *I* think he should'a stayed – an' shot her!'

'You succeeded?' Charlotte said, when I arrived back at our Belgravia office. 'How? That place was supposed to be more difficult to get into than Fort Knox.'

'My natural insinuating charm,' I replied.

'Don't be ridiculous, Richard. How did you really do it?'

'I must say, for somebody who's only been working for me for about thirty-six hours, you don't overdo the flattery do you?'

'Mr Harton,' she said, putting on her glasses and looking very serious, 'from the first moment we met, I recognised you as the sort of person who would be unimpressed by that sort of superficiality.'

'Not at all – I consider it essential.'

'Then you've got the wrong secretary, honey,' she said, removing the spectacles and beaming brightly. 'Anyway, how did you persuade Cruella de Ville to let you in?'

'I pumped the solicitor for a lot of background information on the divorce yesterday and he told me they were in the middle of negotiating a settlement figure.'

'Yes.'

'And that Mrs Dennison wanted to keep the London house and its contents intact as part of her settlement.'

'Yes.'

'So, the lower the valuation is on the house and contents, the bigger her cash balance on the settlement will be.'

'Oh, I see! So, it was in her interest to allow you to inspect everything, because then you'd put on lower figures than if you'd worked from the inventory and assumed that all the pieces were genuine.'

'In theory, yes,' I said.

'What do you mean, "in theory"?' she asked.

'Well, as it turned out, most of the things in the house were very nice, so I put on some fairly hefty values anyway.'

'So, the figures you've put on are over the top after all?'

'Wash your mouth out!' I said. 'No, they're not over the top. But you can bet your life that Hermione has had her own valuer in there, and that the sort of values he's put down are based on what the things would make if they were sold in a marquee, in John O'Groats, during a snow storm, at around lunchtime on Christmas Day.'

'Not a lot?'

'Exactly. Therefore, to redress the balance a little, my valuation is based on the premise that slightly more favourable conditions would prevail at the time of sale.'

'You mean there'd be a series of new world records?'

'Not a series, no . . . just one or two . . . or perhaps three or four . . .'

'So the Dennisons each employ a valuer. They each get a valuation of the same items. And the totals of the two valuations make it look as though one of you went to the wrong address. What then?'

'If they have any sense, they sit down and agree a figure somewhere between the two.'

'And if they don't have any sense?' she asked.

'They could call in an arbitrator or they could just sell

6

the lot and take the cash – they can't argue about the values then.'

'What do you think will happen?'

'I don't know,' I said, 'but I know what should have happened.'

'What's that?'

'Oh, like Molly said – he should have shot her!'

Charlotte looked serious for a moment, then giggled. It was an effervescent giggle which suited her perfectly. Freckled and red-headed, she was frenetic, funny, and honest to the point of being blunt. The previous day she had given me a fearlessly candid series of thumbnail sketches of leading people at Hampson's. It was true that so far I'd only really met one of the subjects – Robert Derby, the chairman – but she'd certainly seemed spot on about him. I was convinced that Charlotte was going to be an invaluable ally over the next few months as I settled into my new and strange surroundings.

Chapter 2

My arrival in London, the day before the Dennison valuation, had quickly brought home to me just how very different to Sussex it was all going to be.

To begin with, Hampson's looked every inch the smart, London auctioneers. Behind its cast-iron railings, the elegant façade of their Vanbrugh Street salerooms was a statement of restrained good taste. A far cry from my old auction rooms in Kington with its permanently peeling paintwork and leaking roof.

A polished brass plaque beside the open mahogany doors read: 'Hampson & Company Ltd – Fine Art Auctioneers – Founded 1865'. Behind the façade, the building's four floors were divided into a complex network of reception areas, salerooms and offices. Staff seemed to be everywhere. The place was like an anthill.

Because ours was judged an ancillary service, it had been decided that the valuations operation didn't need to be housed in the main building. As a result, on that cold January morning, Charlotte Morrison and I had found ourselves sitting in what until a few weeks earlier had been a stationery store in a building one door down the street from the saleroom. Our empire comprised two flights of steep, mainly uncarpeted stairs, an office, a small galley kitchen and a lavatory with a very noisy cistern. It was the sort of accommodation which estate agents describe as 'compact' and 'full of character'.

There was no doubt that Charlotte knew far more about what was going on than I did. Whereas she had worked for Hampson's for just over a year, and had been getting the valuations office ready for habitation since before Christmas, my knowledge was limited to what the Chairman had told me during my two interviews. What it boiled down to was that Hampson's had never really had a department specialising in fee-paying valuation work; now they were going to have one, and I was the person chosen to get it off the ground.

'There's a hell of a lot of work out there, Richard,' Bob Derby had said, gesturing over his shoulder to the street outside his pine-panelled office. 'All you have to do is go out there and get it.'

That was all I had to do. He made it sound very easy, and like all genuinely enthusiastic men he made it sound very convincing. I left his office after our last meeting, in November, intoxicated by his self-confidence and in no doubt as to the inevitability of my eventual success. By January I'd had more than enough time to sober up.

'How many valuation bookings have already been taken for this year?' I asked Charlotte, as we had our first cup of coffee of the morning.

'For the whole of the coming year?'

'Yes.'

'Hold on, I'll have to check,' she said, opening the diary. 'Now let me see . . . January . . . hum . . . March . . . April . . . mmm . . . May . . . uh huh . . . ' she muttered as she flicked through the pages, ' . . . September . . . November . . . December . . . mmm . . . ' At last she closed the book. 'Three,' she said, with a cherubic smile.

'Three! You're joking!'

'Afraid not – three it is.'

'Terrific. That's a great start,' I said. 'What are they like?'

'Well, there's a divorce settlement job tomorrow that Patrick Faulkner tried to do before Christmas but gave up on.'

9

'Why?'

'The wife wouldn't let him in. Normally I wouldn't blame her, knowing Patrick, but on this occasion he assured me he was on his best behaviour.'

'What do you mean?'

'Patrick's a letch – a groper of the old school. You could be standing in the middle of a deserted aircraft hangar and he'd still find a reason why he had to be squeezed up next to you breathing down your bosom.'

'Really?'

'Yes. Well, not in your case, no – he's not that way inclined as far as I'm aware but no woman's safe with him. His hands wander so much they must need an "A to Z" to find their way home some nights.'

'I see,' I said. 'When am I due at this valuation?'

'Tomorrow morning at ten, in Chelsea.'

'Okay, I'll do some homework on that one.'

'The next,' she went on, 'is supposed to be an insurance valuation for a Mrs Popkiewicz in Highgate. That's on Thursday.'

'Why do you say supposed to be?'

'Oh, it's just that it was booked in through Charles Morrison-Whyte, the Pictures Director. And if I know Charlie, if it had been any good, he would have done it himself.'

'What's he like?' I asked.

'Late fifties, lean, mean with his money, supposed to be very knowledgeable and respected in the trade.'

'You don't like him.'

'He once complained to Bob Derby that I was a cocky little madam.'

'What a nerve.'

'That's what I thought,' she agreed. 'Now, the last valuation is next week and it's for insurance purposes, and . . . are you sitting comfortably?'

'Yes.'

'It's for a bookmaker . . .'

'As in leather bindings and gold block lettering?'

'No, silly! As in odds of 10-1 and first past the post.'

'That's what I was afraid of,' I said. 'Where is it?'

'Er . . . that's the other thing . . . are you sure you're ready for this?'

'I doubt it, but go on anyway.'

'Okay, it's in . . . Catford!'

'Catford?'

'Catford.'

'There are nice parts of Catford, are there?'

'Er . . . no.'

'Fantastic,' I said, draining my cup. 'Well, that really is a tremendous start.'

Over the previous few weeks I had, of course, given a lot of thought as to how I could best seize hold of Hampson's embryonic valuations operation and make it into a dynamic force in its field. But somehow, I'd always assumed there would be something, no matter how skeletal that something might be, on which I could build. Although Bob Derby had explained at our first meeting that all valuation work in the past had been done on an ad hoc basis, I had still expected a company over a hundred years old to give me a better start than three valuations – and one of those in Catford. It seemed that I might have underestimated the task before me.

'Not too good is it?' Charlotte commented.

'No, it's not,' I replied. 'But never mind. Where I'm going to get the business from to pay our salaries is currently of secondary importance to another small problem I've got to deal with.'

'What's that?'

'Where I'm going to live.'

'Oh! I'd forgotten. Of course, you've got to get a flat haven't you?'

I had, and quickly. Although I was now in possession of my company car, a daily commute in a not altogether new Mini wasn't my idea of fun. A flat was the only answer. How to find one was the question.

'Anything in this morning's paper?' Charlotte asked.

'Quite a few, but most of them are far too expensive.'

'It does limit one's choice rather, and it's not the best time of the year to be looking either.'

'No,' I said, once again scanning the columns of the newspaper on my desk. 'Still, I think I've got to start going out and seeing some anyway. At least, that way I'll begin to get some idea of what I'll get for my money.'

'Yes, it's difficult to get any sort of accurate picture from the advertisements.'

'It certainly is,' I said. 'Just listen to this: "Primrose Hill, NW1 – fnshed bdsit, bth, CH, £90 pm inc". Now, does that conjure up a vivid picture of a dez rez to you?'

'Quite the opposite,' she said, making a start on her third biscuit. 'Mind you, it has got its own bathroom – that's something. Usually you could expect to share with three or four other individuals, all of whom leave hair in the bath and steal your toothpaste by squeezing it in the middle.'

'Well, I think I should see this place anyway. It's within my budget and it'll be good experience.'

'Okay, I'll try to fix you up with an appointment for early on Thursday on your way to Highgate. It might already be gone by then, but you don't want to live in Primrose Hill anyway.'

'Don't I?'

'No, it's too far north,' Charlotte said, dismissively. 'You need somewhere near here.'

'Belgravia! How much do you think Hampson's are paying me?'

'Well, all right, not actually in the Vanbrugh Street area. But go south rather than north – Battersea or Wandsworth, say.'

'I'll bear it in mind,' I said, 'but fix up the Primrose Hill appointment anyway.'

Chapter 3

It all went quite well until I got to Knightsbridge. My early morning journey in from Sussex had been largely uneventful and I was enjoying driving the Mini. Its legendary manoeuvrability certainly made up for its cramped interior as it nipped in and out of the gathering rush-hour traffic. Ironically, the only problem I'd had during the journey had been as a direct result of that manoeuvrability and my growing self-confidence at the wheel. It was nothing serious. Just that, a few minutes earlier, I had cut in rather sharply in front of a London taxi. The driver had reacted in the way only London cabbies can: with a lengthy blast on the horn and a full, and reasonably accurate appraisal of my driving technique. Undaunted, I acknowledged his comments with the customary two-fingered gesture, and went on my way.

My real difficulty was finding my way around. To get almost anywhere I needed to consult my 'A to Z' street guide almost continuously, and that wasn't easy in heavy, moving traffic. That morning, I knew I needed to head north up Park Lane, and I knew the way onto Park Lane was via Hyde Park Corner. What I wasn't entirely clear about was how to get onto Hyde Park Corner from Knightsbridge. I'd not approached it from that direction before. I glanced down at the 'A to Z' on the passenger seat beside me. There appeared to be a slip-road to the left somewhere. All I had to do was find it.

It's unfortunate that the Mini's mobility isn't equalled by the visibility it allows its driver. That morning I discovered just how difficult it is to spot, let alone read, roadsigns when you are walled into the outer lane of traffic by a seemingly endless convoy of red, double-decker buses. Then, suddenly, the two lanes ahead turned into three. I looked in my mirror – a gap was opening in the traffic to my left. It might be my only chance. I heaved on the wheel and headed for it.

I expect the horns of all London cabs sound roughly the same, but somehow I seemed to recognise the one which blared immediately behind me. As the taxi in question slipped in and filled the slot I'd been aiming for, I caught sight of the driver. As I suspected, it was my critical adversary from half a mile back. He was smiling a very unpleasant smile.

There's nothing wrong with the Hyde Park Corner Underpass. It's a very useful piece of tunnel if you want to travel east-west or west-east. If, however, you're looking to head north or south, it really should be avoided at all costs. As I was sucked, inexorably, into it, my last view of London was of the gaily coloured vehicles above me, bustling around Hyde Park Corner. Then they were gone.

As if being condemned to the underworld wasn't bad enough in itself, I quickly discovered I had another small problem to contend with. It was my old foe in the taxi. He was staying carefully alongside me, hanging out of his window, gesticulating happily and bawling unprintable abuse. I looked, resolutely, straight ahead and tried to smile the sort of confident, knowing, half-smile which suggests that you know something the other person doesn't: in this case, that I'd really *wanted* to drive through the underpass anyway. The uninterrupted howls of derision from my nearside left me in no doubt that my performance was less than convincing. Hyde Park Corner in the rush hour was evidently no place for subtlety.

14

'I thought, perhaps, yew might 'ave changed your mind,'
Mrs Wheatmore said, as she eyed me up and down.

'No, no, ' I assured her, 'it's just that I was delayed by
the traffic.'

'Oh, I know! Yew don't 'ave to tell me. I just dread
going out these days. Cum in, Mr Barton, cum in.'

Despite my professional discipline and years of experience, I couldn't begin to put a date on Mrs Wheatmore.
Her bouffant hair was blacker than jet. It was the sort of
blackness attained only by chemists, never by nature. To
add to the difficulty, her natural complexion was buried
deep beneath a thick mantle of make-up. This resulted in
her looking as though she'd recently been touched up by
an apprentice embalmer. Her manicure was no less
dramatic, with blood-red talons, matching exactly the
glossy application of lipstick about her rather large
mouth. To complete the overall effect, she had obviously
chosen her wardrobe with great care. Her formidable
frame was courageously contained by the tightest
sweater I'd ever seen and a pair of blue jeans that
strained at every seam and gusset.

Accepting her invitation, I stepped into a small hallway
papered with an aggressively large floral print and
embellished with orange woodwork. The colour scheme
sent an involuntary shudder down my spine.

'That's Balthazar,' Mrs Wheatmore informed me, as a
big white Persian cat strolled across the hall and rubbed
against my leg. 'Dew yew like cats, Mr Barton?'

'Yes, yes, I do.'

'Oh, good, I wouldn't trust anyone who didn't, yew
know.'

'No, I don't expect you . . .'

'I did once have a tenant who didn't like cats and 'e was
a thoroughly bad lot.'

'Oh, dear . . .'

15

'Never again, I said to myself.'

'I don't blame . . .'

'No, never again, Pamela, I said.'

'Quite,' I said.

'So, all my gentlemen are cat people.'

'All your gentlemen? You have other tenants, then?'

'Oh, yes. Four at the moment but sometimes there's five.'

'I see,' I said.

'Oh, yes,' she repeated. 'But, what are we doing standing around 'ere chattering – yew want to see the room don't yew?'

'Well, it would be . . .'

'Course yew do! Just follow me – it's on the first floor.'

As I followed Mrs Wheatmore up the stairs, I looked back over my shoulder at the hall. I'd begun to get the uncanny feeling that it was getting smaller. It must have been the wallpaper closing in on me.

The room turned out to be a dreary little box about fifteen feet square. Its high ceiling retained most of the original plasterwork which now served only to make the cubicle more oppressive than it might otherwise have been. A single light hung from the elaborate central rose. The spherical paper shade was the inevitable orange, as were the loudly patterned acrylic curtains.

'I always think it's best not to overfurnish a room,' Mrs Wheatmore observed as I inspected the few sticks of cheap furniture on offer. 'A few pictures on the wall and yew'll 'ave it just like 'ome.'

'It has its own bathroom, I believe,' I said.

'Yes, just down the 'all. I'll show yew.'

At the far end of the landing there was a door with two frosted glass panels. Behind it lay a sight which was about to snuff out whatever spark of optimism I retained regarding my chances of finding a decent flat in London at a price I could afford.

Immediately Mrs Wheatmore opened the door my

16

nostrils were assaulted by the unmistakable smell of towels that have remained wet and unlaundered for at least a fortnight. It was a filthy, musty, fungal odour, more reminiscent of the forest floor than of residential accommodation in Primrose Hill. The place was cold and running with permanently trapped condensation. On the wall, above the massive Victorian cast-iron bath with its chipped enamel, was an ancient water geyser. A spaghetti of eccentric pipework led to and from it, while inside, a pilot flame, visible through a sooty hole in the rusting case, flickered and popped uncertainly.

'All the 'ot water yew want,' Mrs Wheatmore said, leaning across and turning on one of the taps. An irregular torrent of water gushed noisily into the bath while the geyser remained steadfastly dormant. A split second later there was a colossal 'WHOOMF', and a tongue of flame lashed out through the observation hole, then disappeared again. It was several moments before the shockwaves stopped reverberating through the plumbing elsewhere in the house.

'And this would be my private bathroom?' I asked, as Mrs Wheatmore calmly turned off the tap and straightened her bouffant.

'That's correct,' she confirmed. 'The only person to use this bathroom would be yew . . . and the other two gentlemen on the next floor, of course.'

Judging from the exterior of Mrs Popkiewicz's Highgate home, my second appointment of the morning promised to be even less fruitful than the first. An ugly, modern, concrete and brick block, it loomed over the neighbouring houses like some sort of bleak mausoleum. Although it couldn't have been an easy achievement for the architect, the inside was even more depressing than the outside. It was completely devoid of character. Same paint, carpet, and faint smell of old cooking and new carbolic throughout. Every deserted floor looked the same: two rows of identical, polished wood doors, each one with its little white numbers and its little fish-eye security spyhole. These were not the surroundings in which art collections were housed.

I located flat three hundred and nineteen, pressed the doorbell and waited. After a while I thought I heard a faint scuffling noise on the other side of the door, but then it fell silent again. I stepped closer to the door and listened but there was nothing. All I could hear were the faint strains of a radio or record player somewhere else in the building. I pressed the doorbell again.

This time the scuffling started almost immediately. I was certain it was a person, not a cat or a dog. This was not the sort of block that permitted cats or dogs. The noise stopped just as abruptly as before, but this time I just knew there was somebody there. Once more I pressed the doorbell.

'Go 'vay!' The voice was thin and reedy and came from immediately the other side of the door.

'Mrs Popkiewicz?'

'Go 'vay!'

'Mrs Popkiewicz – it's Richard Harton from Hampson's.'

'Go 'vay, I call da police.'

'Mrs Popkiewicz, you requested an insurance valuation of some pictures . . .'

'Go 'vay, I don't know you . . . leaf me alone . . . I call da police . . . dey on der vay . . . ' She began to sob as she spoke.

What a day! So far I'd been verbally assaulted by an irate cabby, subjected to the full horrors of a London bedsit, and now I was about to be arrested for terrorising an old lady in her own home. And it wasn't even midday yet.

'Mrs Popkiewicz,' I persevered, in my most caring and soothing tone, 'I think you may have arranged the appointment with Charles Morrison-Whyte.'

There was a pause in the sobbing. 'Vot you say?'

'I said, I believe you may have arranged the appointment with Charles Morrison-Whyte.'

There was renewed scuffling followed by the sound of the door being unlocked. Next, it opened an inch or two and a wizened, sick-looking face peered cautiously round it.

'Who you zay you are?' asked Mrs Popkiewicz.

'I'm Richard Harton. I'm the new manager of Hampson's valuations office.'

'Vy I never zin you before?'

'As I said,' I explained, 'I'm new to Hampson's. I think you made this appointment with Charles Morrison-Whyte.'

'I didn't make no appointment.'

'Well, obviously, wires have got crossed somewhere,' I said, not entirely broken-hearted at the thought of failing to gain admission to Mrs Popkiewicz's home. 'I'll check what's happened when I get back to the office and perhaps Mr Morrison-Whyte can telephone you when . . .'

'Vait zer!' The door was closed with a bang, chains rattled furiously and then it re-opened. 'Come in! Quick! Quick! Quick! I got no clothez on!'

It was an interesting invitation although not entirely irresistible or accurate. Firstly, Mrs Popkiewicz was tiny, frail, probably about seventy-five and very nearly bald. Secondly, she wore a long white night-dress and pink bed socks.

I stepped inside the flat. She hurriedly closed the door, replacing the chain as she did so.

'Vait 'ere,' she instructed, 'I come back.' She scuttled off down the rather gloomy hall, disappearing into a room at the end and closing the door behind her. Moments later she re-appeared, resplendent in a somewhat tangled auburn wig which made her look a little top-heavy, and a woollen plaid dressing gown which also seemed rather too large. 'Now, vot you doing 'ere?' she demanded.

I explained about the insurance valuation.

'No!' she said, emphatically, 'it vos not me. I did not make no appointment for no valuation.'

'Then, obviously, there has been some mistake on our part,' I said. 'Do accept my apologies, Mrs Popkiewicz. I'll try to find out how this occurred when I get back to the office and . . .'

'You vait!' she ordered. 'Now you're 'ere, you look round.'

This was not what I wanted to hear. I had already wasted most of my morning and I was quite keen on salvaging what little remained of it. A cursory inspection of the hall while Mrs Popkiewicz had been putting her hair on had confirmed my suspicions about the flat: there was nothing there of value at all. One cheap, modern print graced the wall facing the door – it was the only picture in sight. Added to that, all the furniture was cheap 1930s oak. Flat three hundred and nineteen was definitely not the home of a collector.

'Well, I should be getting back,' I protested.

'No, you look round!' she insisted, shuffling across the hall and fumbling with the handle of one of several doors that isolated us from the rest of the flat. Daylight flooded into the hallway as she opened it. 'Come in,' she said, beckoning to me impatiently. 'Come in.'

Generally speaking, the room in which I found myself was no great improvement on the hall. The furniture was the same cheap oak, interspaced with two elderly easy chairs and an old sofa. But the walls were different. They were covered in pictures.

I stopped to examine an interesting oil which was hanging just inside the door. It was a cubist study of a village.

'Vot you sink?' asked Mrs Popkiewicz, in a bored, disinterested tone which was at odds with her insistence

20

that I should stay and look around.

'Good Lord!' I replied, quite unable to hide my surprise. 'It's a Raoul Dufy.'

'Yeah, yeah – vot you sink?'

'I think it's a good example . . . ' I began.

'Yeah, yeah, I know all zat,' she cut in. 'Vot you sink it's vorth?'

'Well, I'd want to check with one of our specialists before I gave a definite figure . . .'

'Yeah, yeah, but vot do *you* sink?' She wasn't sounding so bored or disinterested now.

'Under the hammer – six or eight thousand, perhaps,' I suggested.

She nodded, but looked unimpressed. 'Vot about zat one?' she asked, pointing to a small, impressionistic still life of apples on the other side of the room.

I walked over and looked at it.

'Good Lord!' I said again. 'It's a Renoir.'

'I know vot it is,' replied its owner, sounding bored again. 'Vot's it vorth?'

'Well, it's not one of his major works, of course . . .'

Mrs Popkiewicz looked at me with a pained expression as she slowly lowered herself into one of the chairs.

' . . . but it would certainly make ten to fifteen thousand.'

She took a cigarette from a packet which had been lying on the stained and ring-marked table at the arm of her chair. Lighting it, she picked up a pen from the same table and scribbled something on the back of the packet.

'And zat?' she said, when she had finished writing.

She was pointing to one of the larger pictures in the room.

'Fernand Léger – fifteen to twenty thousand,' I said, beginning to become quite blasé.

Again, Mrs Popkiewicz scribbled a note on the back of

her cigarette packet.

'And zat vun?' she said, without looking up, waving her hand limply in the general direction of what appeared to be an Henri de Toulouse-Lautrec lithograph.

'Have you had a recent insurance valuation made of these pictures, Mrs Popkiewicz?' I asked, as I wandered over to look at the picture.

She was immediately seized by an awful, crackling gurgling coughing fit. Dropping the cigarette packet into her lap, she clutched the arms of her chair and doubled forward as the spasm racked her from head to toe.

'Vot you say?' she spluttered, when she was once again capable of speech.

'I was asking if you'd had a recent insurance valuation made of your pictures.'

'No. Vy you ask?'

'Simply because you have an interesting collection here and it should be properly recorded and insured,' I said.

'Oh, yeah! Oh, yeah!' she said, taking another deep pull on her cigarette. 'An who's goin' to pay for it, Mister? You? 'Cos I tell you – I got no money.'

'I'm afraid you'll have even less if this place is ever burgled.'

'Vot? Vot? Vy you talk 'bout burglars? Vy you try to frighten me?' she said, suddenly upset and agitated.

'I'm sorry, I didn't mean to frighten you,' I assured her. 'It's just that I think you should be aware that you could lose tens of thousands in minutes if anybody broke in here.'

She glared at me and angrily stubbed her cigarette into a dirty glass ashtray on the table by her chair.

'This piece for instance,' I continued, picking up a small bronze group. It was barely six inches high and unmistakable.

'Vot about it?' she asked, at the same time retrieving the cigarette packet from her lap.

'Well, although once again I would want to do some research on it,' I said, turning the piece around in my hand, 'I think you could expect this cast to make a minimum of ten to fifteen thousand pounds.'

'Henry Moore bronze – ten to fifteen sousand,' she muttered, as she scratched away at the back of the cigarette packet. 'And vot about zat vun?' she asked, once again pointing to the Toulouse-Lautrec lithograph.

'Mrs Popkiewicz,' I said, deciding the time had come to discontinue my free valuation service, 'if you would like me to make an insurance valuation of your pictures I would be delighted to arrange it . . .'

'I already tell you – I got no money. I can't afford nothin'.'

' . . . and I would, of course, be happy to quote a flat fee for doing the work.'

'Ha! He talks about a fee!' she moaned, tossing down the cigarette packet and throwing up her hands in despair. 'An' ver am I going to get za money to pay zese fees of yours, Mister? You tell a poor, sick old vidow-vooman zat, eh!' Once again she started to sob gently.

As the tears slowly rolled down Mrs Popkiewicz's grey, sunken cheeks I began to feel for her. And why not? Perhaps she was cantankerous, but what she said was right. She *was* old, she *was*, very obviously, sick, perhaps terminally so, and I had no reason to doubt that she was a widow. That only left her claim to being poverty-stricken not proven.

A fresh series of muffled sobs escaped from behind the almost transparently thin hands that now covered her face.

Wrestling with my conscience, I looked around the room once again, and as I did so, something snapped

23

me back to reality. It was like coming out of an hypnotic trance. Poor! Mrs Popkiewicz? Poor? If only we could all be as poor as Mrs Popkiewicz. She had over a hundred thousand pounds worth of pictures and sculptures in that one little room, and you could bet your boots there was more hidden away elsewhere in the flat. I had to be going soft. She was conning me, and I was letting her get away with it. All she had to do to solve her problem was sell one minor piece and she'd be able to pay Hampson's fee and the new insurance premium, buy herself a decent wig, go on holiday for a couple of weeks and still have change for a packet of cigarettes. There *was* no problem.

'Have you considered parting with one of the less important items,' I suggested.

A sudden, stunned silence fell on the room. Even the heart-breaking sobbing stopped. It was as though the whole world was holding its breath.

'Vot!' Mrs Popkiewicz gasped, as her hands fell to her lap. 'Vot you zay?'

'I asked if you had ever considered parting with one of the minor works – to finance a valuation,' I said, repeating the heresy in even more explicit terms.

She stared at me, open mouthed.

'It would seem the obvious solution,' I went on. 'If, for instance, you sold the Lautrec lithograph over there, you'd realise between three and four thousand and then you could . . .'

'Zell za Lautrec!' she croaked, staggering to her feet. 'Zell za Lautrec! Are you crazy?'

'No, Mrs Popkiewicz, not crazy, just pragmatic.'

'You get out!' she shouted. 'You get outa here! You're tryin' to trick me outa my money. You get outa here, Mister!'

'Certainly,' I said, taking one of my brand new business cards from my wallet and placing it on the ring-stained table, 'but should you change your mind, please don't

24

hesitate to contact me.'

'You get outa here!' she repeated, shooing me ahead of her as she shuffled into the hall.

I opened the flat door and stepping into the corridor turned to say goodbye.

'You vait zer!' Mrs Popkiewicz ordered, as I opened my mouth. Then she scuttled off, back into the sitting room, returning moments later with the cigarette packet and pen. 'Now, Mister,' she went on, pen poised, 'vot you zay za Lautrec's vorth?'

Despite having two large windows overlooking Vanbrugh Street, Charles Morrison-Whyte's office was really quite dark. The series of tall mahogany bookcases which housed his considerable reference library were chiefly responsible, but the pall of expensive cigar smoke that hung in the air also made a significant contribution to the gloom. With its leather-upholstered chairs and large mahogany desk, it was more like the library of a gentlemen's club than an office.

Morrison-Whyte rose to receive me as I entered. He was of medium height and lean build with a rather pale complexion. His silver-grey hair was swept back from his high, lined forehead giving him a vaguely professorial air. That, however, was countered by his immaculate three-piece suit which hinted at the income of a merchant banker. Whatever salary the director of Hampson's picture department was on, it was a lot larger than mine.

'Hello,' he said, as I introduced myself, 'I've been meaning to pop next door to see you, but you know how it is.' He resumed his seat and pointed to one of the leather chairs. 'Do sit down. How are you finding things?'

'Oh, I'm only just starting to find my way around.'

'Of course, of course,' he said, smiling, as he picked

up a jade paperknife from the desk and turned it slowly in his hands.

'I really wanted to talk to you about a Mrs Popkiewicz,' I said.

'Oh, no!' he said, throwing the paperknife back onto his blotter and holding up his hands in protest. 'Not Mrs Popkiewicz!'

'Why? What's the story?'

'No story. No story at all – other than the fact that the wretched woman's a complete nuisance. How do you know her?'

'I've just been to see her.'

'Why, for God's sake? She's a complete and utter waste of time.'

'Chiefly because you booked an insurance valuation for her in my diary.'

'I did what?' He looked blank. Then the look changed to one of comprehension. 'You're right,' he said. 'I did. Oh damn it. I meant to tell that idiot girl of yours to ignore it. I do apologise, Richard. I'm afraid you'll just have to write it off to experience.'

'But what was it all about?' I asked.

'Oh, the bloody woman's a menace. She's constantly trying to get free valuations of her pictures. I should think she tries every auctioneer and dealer in town once every couple of months – doesn't get very far of course, she's too well known.'

'But why does she do it?'

'She just wants to gloat over what they're worth, and I think she gets some enjoyment out of writing insulting letters to the people who advise lower values than she wants to hear. You didn't waste too much time on her, I hope?'

'No, not really. Actually, I was quite glad to have had the opportunity to see her collection.'

'Yes, she's got some good stuff. It was all collected by her late husband. I don't think she has any understanding of it – it's just pounds and pence to her. Not that she'll ever sell any of it. It'll all go to Battersea Dogs Home or the like when she goes.'

'Which won't be long if the way she looked this morning's anything to go by,' I commented.

'You could be right, but she's looked awful for years – emphysema, I think.' He smiled and picked up a notepad and pen from his desk. 'Now, is there anything else I can do for you, Richard? I must get down to some cataloguing.'

'Er . . . well, I was still wondering how the appointment found its way into my diary to begin with.'

'What? Oh, that.' He stood up. 'It was simply a mistake on the part of a new porter of mine. Anyway, your Miss Morrison should have realised it was all nonsense. If I was you I'd keep an eye on her. She can be pretty sloppy.'

'Sloppy! Sloppy! The arrogant old toad!'

It was the first time I'd seen Charlotte lose her temper, and it was not a pretty sight.

'There was nothing sloppy about it,' she went on, her colour still rising. 'His office made a cock-up and he unloaded it onto us because he was too idle to sort it out.'

'Never mind . . .'

'But I *do* mind,' she said, banging her desk. 'He's got no right to blame me. How on earth was I to know this Popwatsit woman . . .'

'Popkiewicz,' I suggested.

'. . . yes, exactly . . . well, how was I supposed to know she was a fraud? I've never worked in the pictures department.'

'Forget it,' I said. 'It doesn't matter.'

Charlotte continued to simmer quietly as her colour slowly returned to normal.

'Anyway,' I said, 'you did tell me Charles Morrison-

27

Whyte would never give us a decent valuation introduction.'

'That's a point,' she replied, brightening up. 'I hope you mentioned that to him.'

'No, I didn't think it would be good for inter-office diplomatic relations to be broken off at this early stage.'

'Huh!' Charlotte snorted in disgust.

'Oh, by the way – would I be right in assuming Charlie-boy's loaded?' I asked.

'You mean the cigars and the expensive wardrobe?'

'Yes.'

'I understand he married money.'

'Well, lucky old him,' I said. 'I'm beginning to think that's the only way I'll ever be able to afford a flat.'

'Oh! Sorry, Richard,' Charlotte said, 'with all the fuss about Mrs Popthingavitch, I forgot to ask. How was Primrose Hill?'

'Don't ask.'

'That bad, uh?'

'Worse – it was gruesome. If that's what accommodation in London's like, I'm in big trouble.'

'Not when you've got a fairy godmother like me, you're not.'

'Charlotte, what are you talking about?'

'Well, I almost forgot,' she began. 'I've got some good news and some bad news for you. Which would you like first?'

I wasn't really in the mood for guessing games, but I hadn't got the strength to argue either. 'I think I'm due for some good – go on, what is it?'

'I've found you a reasonably civilised temporary home if you'd like it.'

'Lead me to it! Where is it?'

'Wandsworth. My brother, Tom, shares a house with three friends, and one of them's decided to be a ski-bum for the season. So, they're looking for somebody to take his room till the middle of April. I thought it might make life a bit more bearable until you find a place of your own.'

'Charlotte – you are a genius.'

'I know,' she said, 'I'm invaluable.'

'I'll mention that to Charles Morrison-Whyte next time I see him,' I replied. 'By the way, what's the bad news?'

'Oh, it's just that everybody in the flat's mad, especially my brother.'

'That shouldn't prove a problem,' I said. 'I've been hovering on the brink myself all day.'

Chapter 4

'Is that you, Richard?' Tom Morrison called from the sitting room as I let myself in.

'Yes.'

'Good. Now you're not allowed to go skulking off to your bed straight away. As your temporary landlord I insist that you join me for a nightcap.'

Charlotte had been quite right about her brother: he was quite mad. He was also generous and amusing, but most of all he was mad, as indeed were his flatmates. They were all brokers of one sort or another in the City and seemed to live on their nerves and adrenalin. Now they would be classed as Yuppies, then they fell into the Sloane Ranger genus. They all dressed alike, talked alike, drove the same sort of cars and shared a seemingly bottomless pool of mutual friends and acquaintances, all of whom had strange nicknames like Twonky, Plonky and Winky. For an outsider like myself, these resolutely asexual names made the group's conversations extremely difficult to follow. After expending a lot of time and effort in trying to sort out who was doing what, and with which, and to whom, I eventually gave up on the grounds that the possible permutations had become improbably exotic. This left me at a bit of a loose end when it came to chatting with my new co-habitees since, as a body, they seemed to talk of nothing else. Empires might crumble and economies crash, but conversation amongst the boys remained rigidly confined to such urgent topics as what Binky had done to Winky at Twonky's house party the previous weekend.

The other thing that set them apart was the sheer physicality of their leisure activities. It wasn't just that they played rugby and squash; it was the way they could make a game of chess resemble the D-Day landings. The first time I went out with them to the local trattoria, I suddenly found myself caught in a fusillade of bread rolls and pasta. I never found out what started it, but it nearly wrecked the restaurant, did no end of good for the local dry-cleaners and left Tom and myself to eventually shake off our pursuers by hiding among some particularly foul-smelling dustbins. After almost a week of this doggedly jolly, but otherwise rather arid new way of life, I longed for a quiet evening reading a book. Since it seemed to me that the chances of managing that were nil, I had just taken myself off to a cheap little bistro, out of Tom's normal orbit, where I had enjoyed a singularly peaceful meal. It was while I was in the act of sneaking back from there to my bed and book that Tom heard me.

He was sitting alone contemplating an unbroached bottle of scotch. The television was on and the floor was littered with the day's newspapers and three or four glossy magazines. It looked dangerous: all the signs suggested that, deprived of companionship, Tom Morrison was bored.

'My dear old thing,' he beamed, 'where have you been? I hope that slave-driving sister of mine hasn't been making you over-work. You'll have to watch her – she's a real Tartar.'

'No, nothing to do with Charlotte. I had to meet somebody about a possible valuation,' I lied.

'Oh, how dreary. Never mind, all the more reason for having a decent snifter now.'

'It's very kind of you to offer, Tom, but I've got an important valuation to do tomorrow and . . .'

'So what? One won't hurt you. It'll be medicinal – it'll make sure you get a good night's sleep.'

'Well . . .'

'Look, what's the time now?' he said, glancing at his watch. 'Well, there you are, it's only just gone nine o'clock. One quick nip of Scottish wine and you'll be in the arms of Morpheus by half-past.'

It was a little after one-thirty the following morning when Tom tipped the dregs of the bottle into my glass. In the absence of his normal gang he had been happy to widen the topics of conversation, and we had discussed everything from the advantages of strict monetary controls in a free economy, to the undesirability of traffic wardens in a free society. By the time we helped one another upstairs, we were in total agreement about most major world issues and a host of minor ones as well.

The buzzer on my alarm stabbed through the shroud of sleep like a jagged knife. Semi-conscious, I groped blindly to end the offensive noise, succeeding only in knocking half a glass of water off the bedside table into the bed. The ice-cold shock brought me round in an instant. At the same moment I became aware of an acute pain somewhere behind my left eye: small men with needle-sharp pick-axes were apparently trying to break out of what little remained of my brain by digging a tunnel through the back of my eyeball. I allowed my eyelids to grate closed again but it didn't help. It was clear that my only chance of relief lay in soluble aspirin. I stumbled to the bathroom, gulped down a pint and a half of water and raided the medicine cabinet. Four aspirin later I stood, regarding myself in the mirror, wondering why on earth I'd done it. The answer, of course, was the same as ever: it had seemed a good idea at the time.

With trembling hand I expertly lacerated my face

with a new razor-blade, then hauled myself into the steaming shower to staunch the flow of blood. Only in the shower did I begin to believe that my condition might not be terminal.

The morning was crisp and very cold, with both the car and the road covered in a thick hoar-frost. Hands still shaking, I took a credit card from my wallet and started to scrape the ice crust from the windscreen and windows. Twice, as I walked around the vehicle, I almost slipped and fell. The drive to Belgravia promised to be interesting.

No sooner had I got into the car than my breath condensed, then froze on the cold windscreen – quite surprising considering the likely alcohol content of each lungful. Once again I chipped away with my faithful credit card, although it was obvious the screen was only going to stay clear once the heater was working. As soon as I'd cleared an area large enough to see through I turned the ignition key. There was a dull clunk from somewhere under the bonnet. The warning lights momentarily gave off the faintest of glimmers then all was quiet: the battery was absolutely dead.

I have never reacted well to the failure of any machine. The breakdown of anything from a tin-opener to a jumbo jet has always brought out the worst in me, and the deficiency in my 'new' company car was no exception. I beat the steering wheel and stamped wildly on the pedals. Strangely, this did no good at all, although the frequency of the jabs of pain behind my left eye increased in line with my blood pressure. In an attempt to put an end to both the discomfort and the blinding flashes which were now also a feature of my physical condition, I allowed my eyes to crash shut again. As a sort of calm descended, so reason returned, and I accepted that what I actually needed was help. I looked up and down the street. It was deserted. There was only one thing for it: I had to raise Tom Morrison from his bed.

33

That morning it would probably have been easier to raise Lazarus. I banged loudly on my landlord's bedroom door without receiving any response.

'Tom!' I shouted.

Still no response.

'Tom!'

Still no sound from the other side of the door. I opened it and went into the darkened room. By the landing light I could make out a bed on the other side of the room. In the middle of it was an irregular mound which appeared to be made up of sheets, blankets and an eiderdown. Sticking out from under it was a foot; seemingly the only part of Tom Morrison to have survived the previous night's excesses.

'Tom!'

The foot showed no sign of having heard me.

'TOM!' I bellowed, shaking the mound roughly. 'WAKE UP!'

'Wha? . . . whasamadder? . . . whatsamatter? . . . oh, God! . . . my head! . . . ' croaked a voice, somewhere deep inside the pile of bedclothes.

'I need you to help start my car, Tom,' I said. 'The battery's flat and I've got to get to the office early.'

'Wha? . . . oh, God! . . . what time is it for Chrissake?'

'Almost seven,' I said.

The foot stirred, then disappeared beneath the mound. At the same time a great general eruption took place which resulted in the abrupt appearance of the dishevelled head and shoulders of the incumbent.

'Seven o'clock?' he rasped. 'Seven o'clock? Christ! Have a heart, Richard. God, I feel awful. Why's my foot so bloody cold? What did we do last night?'

'We had a quiet night in,' I replied.

'Quiet? Well, that's more than can be said for my head now – it's hammering away like J. Arthur Rank's gong.' Slowly he collapsed back onto the bed and allowed his eyes to close.

'Tom!' I said, shaking him by the shoulder.

'Wha! Oh, do pack that in, Richard, there's a good chap. I just can't take it this morning. I'm going to have to ring in sick . . .'

'Tom!'

'Wha!'

'Tom, you must help me bump-start my car. I really must get to the office.'

'Oh, for God's sake!'

'Please, Tom.'

'Oh, all right, all right. If it's the only thing that'll get rid of you. Pass me my dressing gown – it's bloody freezing.'

A few minutes later, Tom Morrison was positioned behind my car. He wore a brown trilby hat and a navy blue overcoat. Below that, his bare white legs terminated in black Gucci shoes. He was the ultimate in Wandsworth *haute couture*.

'I'll give you a hand to push it out of the parking space,' I said, 'and then . . .'

'Oh, just get in the bloody thing, Richard. I can push a bloody Mini without any bloody help – even in my current weakened bloody state.'

'If you're sure . . .'

'For Chrissake get on with it! I'm beginning to lose all sense of feeling in vital parts of my anatomy.'

Doing as I was told, I got into the car, put it in neutral, turned on the ignition and let off the handbrake. 'Okay,' I shouted. 'Push!'

Nothing happened. I looked in the rear-view mirror but there was no sign of my landlord. Once again I turned off the ignition, pulled on the handbrake and got out of the car. There was indeed no sign of Tom, but in the early morning quiet I could hear heavy breathing punctuated by earthy, monosyllabic curses coming from somewhere. I found their originator lying face-down on the road clinging by his fingertips to the back bumper of the car.

'Did you slip?' I asked.

'No, no, I just thought I'd take the opportunity to catch up on a little sleep,' he replied, without looking up. Then, raising his head and fixing me with horrible bloodshot eyes, he went on: 'Of course I bloody slipped!'

I was still going through the 'Flats to Rent' columns of *The Times* when Charlotte arrived at the office. I had already heavily circled one advertisement.

'You're in early,' Charlotte said.

'Yes, I've got to be in darkest Catford by nine, and I wanted to go through the flats before I go.'

'Anything any good?' she asked, looking over my shoulder.

'Yes,' I said, 'this one: "Kensington W8 – self-contained flat in private house, bed, kit, bthrm, shared entrance – £25pw inc."'

'Interesting,' Charlotte said, re-reading the advertisement. 'Have you telephoned?'

'Not yet. I thought it was too early, but I'll give them a call before I leave for Catford.'

'I should ring now. There'll be a lot of people after it – it's the early bird and all that stuff.'

I looked at my watch – a quarter to eight. 'Perhaps you're right,' I said. 'I'll call them now.'

By a quarter-past eight I felt I couldn't put off my departure for Catford any longer. 'Damn it!' I said, slamming down the telephone.

'Still engaged?' Charlotte asked.

'Yes, for a solid half hour, and I must get going or I'll be late. Damn it! Damn it! Damn it!'

'Don't worry, I'll keep trying until I get through. If the flat's still up for grabs I'll make an appointment for you. What time shall I suggest?'

'Difficult to say. For all I know this valuation could take all day.'

'Why don't I say six o'clock then?'

'All right, but if there are any problems just ring me at Catford – you've got the number.'

Clearly, Mr Frank Boston was not one of life's smilers. Although his small, chimp-like face was heavily lined, the crow's-feet, generally present on the faces of those of a happy disposition, were markedly absent. He was not much over five feet three or four and was slightly built, but he had an air about him which suggested he was not to be toyed with. Furthermore, if Mr Boston was small, everything else in his life appeared to be very big. His house – more Bromley than Catford – was a modern, neo-Georgian, eight-bedroomed gin palace which dwarfed the neighbouring properties, and boasted a huge white portico which would have been more in scale on Castle Howard or Blenheim. Parked on the red tarmac outside the double garage was a glistening one-year-old Rolls Royce. A Mercedes convertible stood next to it. The garden at the rear of the house appeared to be given over almost entirely to a large, amoeba-shaped swimming pool which was evidently a recent addition, since two men were still working on the paving around it.

'How do you want to go about it, Mr Harton?' my client asked, as we stood beneath about four thousand pounds' worth of brand new chandelier in the entrance hall.

'I'll just check the details first, then perhaps you could quickly show me round, and then I'll get on with the job.'

'All right.'

'Firstly,' I said, consulting my notes, 'I understand you want a valuation of the entire contents for insurance purposes.'

'Yes.'

'Fine. What I normally do is to describe and value individually any items of importance in each room and then put on a lump-sum at the end to cover the remaining pieces. Would you be happy with that?'

'Yes.'

'Good. Now . . . just glancing around, it strikes me that a lot of things have been purchased recently.'

'Yes.'

'Do you still have records of what you paid?'

'Yes.' Although Mr Boston's expression didn't change, his eyes narrowed a little.

'The reason I ask is because it will save a lot of time if I don't have to run around the retailers checking prices to find out what the current replacement values are.'

'Yes, I can see that.'

'So, would you have any objection to my consulting your records?'

'Well, that depends.' His expression still remained unchanged and as inscrutable as any oriental, but his eyes seemed to become brighter and more piercing.

'On what?' I asked.

'On what's in it for me.'

'I'm sorry, I'm not sure what you mean, Mr Boston,' I said, almost certain that I knew exactly what he meant.

'Well, your fee is charged as a percentage of the overall valuation total, isn't it?'

'Yes.'

'So, whether you have to spend days running around Harrods and the General Trading Company, or whether you just spend an hour sitting down at my desk going through all my receipts, I'll end up paying the same – right?'

'Well . . . yes,' I said, in the absence of any worthwhile counter-argument.

'So, what's in it for me – for making your life easier, Mr Harton? I think they call it a quid pro quo, don't they?'

'I believe they do,' I replied, a little frostily.

'So what's it worth?' he persisted, quietly, still holding me with those cold eyes.

Just how I'd allowed myself to get involved in negotiations like this I wasn't at all sure. What I did know was that they were going very badly. It was all terribly discomforting, and what was more, my hangover was coming back. I needed more aspirin.

'Er . . . ' I said, as images of warm beds and darkened rooms came and went, 'well . . .'

'Yes?'

'Well . . . let me have a look at what's involved and I'll quote you a flat fee.'

'That sounds fair enough, Mr Harton,' he said, with just the faintest suggestion of a smile. 'That's all I ask: just a little quid pro quo.'

I stumbled through the house behind my client, feeling weaker by the moment. The whole place was stuffed full of Maples reproduction, Chinese carpets, onyx and ormolu, cut glass and Capo di Monte figures – not the sort of stuff for a man with a headache and a gippy tummy. It was all brand new and all horribly expensive. I had no doubt that the curtains alone would have seen off my whole year's salary. The most expensive item of all, however, didn't fall within my remit: it was Mrs Boston. She was just leaving the drawing room when we were going in. She was blonde and had the looks, figure and height of a model. This meant she dwarfed her husband. She also appeared to be a good twenty years his junior.

'Hello, Frankie,' she said, in a refined cockney accent. 'I'm just popping out to do a little shopping, sweetheart. See you this evening.'

'This evening!' her husband groaned, with something near to a show of emotion. 'How can you call all day a *little* shopping?'

'Oh, don't go on, Frankie. I'm meeting Trish; you know how quick the time'll go once we start gossiping.'

'I know how quick my money'll go once you two get up West,' he muttered morosely. He stared at her sullenly for a moment then seemed to remember I was still there. 'Oh, by the way, this is Mr Harton from Hampson's – he's come to do the valuation. This is my

39

wife, Susie, Mr Harton.'

'Pleased to meet you,' Susie Boston murmured, glancing at me momentarily before turning her attention back to her husband. 'You don't really mind do you, Frankie? You know how miserable I get when I get bored.'

Frank Boston didn't reply. Instead he just looked a little tired and allowed himself to be pecked on the forehead like a small boy being despatched to school.

'Byee, Frankie,' his wife cooed. 'See you this evening – be good.' Her ultra-high heels tick-tacked their way across the entrance hall's Italian tile floor. I watched in silent appreciation as her long brown legs carried her out of the front door towards the waiting Mercedes.

'You married?' Her husband's voice interrupted my thoughts and reminded me I'd still got a hangover.

'No, no, I'm not.'

'Very wise. You stay that way if you don't want a load of hassle – you take my word for it.'

'Right,' I said, wondering just what it was Frankie got in return for his particular load of hassle.

'So, what's your verdict?'

'Sorry?'

'What's your charge for doing this lot?' He had reverted to the sordid subject of commerce while I was still busy picturing those extraordinarily long, brown legs being eased gracefully into the Mercedes convertible.

'Ah, yes,' I said, trying to forget both Susie Boston and the newly rediscovered stabbing pain behind my left eye. 'Three hundred and twenty-five pounds, plus VAT.'

'All right,' he said, straight away, 'sounds fair enough to me. Where do you want to start?'

'Upstairs.'

'Okay – anything you need?'

'Well, since you mention it . . . would you happen to have any soluble aspirin?'

Apart from being excrutiatingly boring, the actual valuation went well and, with the exception of going

40

through the receipts to check my figures, I'd finished it before half-past one.

'Take them with you if it's easier,' Mr Boston said, handing me the thick file of accounts, 'then I can get back to work. I must drop into a couple of my shops in Romford. I find the occasional surprise visit helps takings no end.'

'How many betting shops have you got?' I asked.

'Fifteen at the moment, but it goes up and down. Just depends on how things are going. I still prefer working the tracks myself but that wouldn't pay for this lot – or her ladyship's shopping trips come to that,' he paused. 'That reminds me, are you any good on jewellery?'

'No,' I said, immediately. Although I did have some knowledge of Victorian and Edwardian jewellery, I was by no means an expert, and since the opportunities for making major mistakes were considerable, I always made it clear it wasn't my field. 'But, if you want me to arrange for Mrs Boston's collection to be valued,' I continued, 'I'd be happy to set it up with our specialist.'

'No, it's not that. I've got a trade contact in Hatton Garden who looks after all that for me. It's just one thing I want checked, and my man's away for a couple of weeks.'

'What is it?'

'That's what I need to know. Hold on here for a minute. I'll get it.' He disappeared out of the room, returning a few minutes later with a small, draw-string, chamois-leather bag. 'It's in there,' he said. 'Tell me what you think.'

The bag contained a gold ring set with a large yellow stone. The stone was cut in the way one would cut an emerald – rectangular with chamfered edges, shoulders and corners.

'I would have thought it was a topaz,' I said. 'What's it supposed to be?'

'It's supposed to be a canary-coloured diamond, and if

41

it isn't, somebody's in very serious trouble.'

'Well, for goodness' sake don't take my word for it,' I said, suspecting that serious trouble in Frank Boston's book might have something to do with becoming an integral part of the nearest motorway extension. 'After all, it must weigh several carats, which is going to make it worth a lot of money if it is a diamond.'

We both stood looking at the ring. The more I looked at it, the more uncertain I became. It certainly could have been a diamond, but the shoulders were chipped in several places and there was some surface scratching, all of which suggested a much softer stone. I'd have put my money on it being a topaz, but I got the impression that Frankie had already backed it heavily on the nose as a diamond.

'I can take it with me and get it checked this afternoon if you'd like me to,' I said.

'Yes, all right,' he replied, without lifting his eyes from the ring, 'but I must have it back by five at the latest. That's essential.' He looked up and fixed me once again with those expressionless, glacial eyes. 'Absolutely essential,' he repeated.

It was just then that I realised that Frank Boston, little Frankie Boston, scared the living daylights out of me. There was something about his whole, quietly con-trolled manner which suggested absolute ruthlessness.

'No problem,' I said, inexplicably agreeing to a deadline which I knew, at the outset, would be a very great problem. 'Would you like it included in the house inventory?' I asked, as I stepped out under the massive portico.

'No, no, I don't want any mention of it at all,' he said, quickly. 'I don't even need to know what it's worth. I'll follow my nose on that. All I want you to tell me is whether it's a diamond or not.'

I must have looked puzzled.

'This is business,' he went on, by way of explanation.

'Nothing to do with my home or my wife. It's just business.'

'I understand,' I said, not understanding at all, but not wanting to get any more involved than I already was.

'I took that rock you've got in your pocket in payment of an old debt run up by one of my regular punters,' he continued. 'I took his word that it was a diamond, and I took his word that it'll clear all his outstanding with some change left over. Now you've sown a seed of doubt, Mr Harton, and since I learnt about an hour ago that the gentleman concerned is moving house suddenly this evening without leaving a forwarding address, I'd just like to have my mind put at rest.' The menace was now almost palpable, and yet neither his expression nor tone of voice had changed one bit since we first met. 'I just don't like being taken for a mug, Mr Harton,' he went on, as if I needed that particular point spelt out, 'like that bloke over there – he thinks I'm a mug, and I don't like it.'

The man he referred to was one of the two who were paving the swimming pool area. He was collecting a bag of cement from their van in the road outside.

'It's only a little thing, but it annoys me,' Frank Boston went on. 'Every now and then I offer him and his mate a cigar – good ones too. His mate always takes his and lights up, and this bloke always takes his, sticks it behind his ear and says he'll have it later.'

'Yes,' I said, not really sure what the problem was.

'You don't see it, do you?'

'No.'

'Shows you weren't brought up in Whitechapel. He doesn't smoke, Mr Harton. I'd put money on it. He keeps it until I've gone then gives it to his mate. He thinks I'm a mug.'

'Well, perhaps not, Mr Boston,' I said, trying to muster some sort of defence on the man's behalf. 'He

43

might just prefer to smoke it later – in the evening, say, after he's eaten.'

'Oh, you mean he sits down and savours it with his vintage port after his Chateaubriand steak.'

'Something like that,' I said.

'I think you're crediting our friend with social graces which would be altogether foreign to him, Mr Harton. But let's see which of us is right – fancy a little flutter?'

'No thanks.'

'Wise man, Mr Harton. Wise man.'

Blissfully unaware of the conversation which had been taking place, the man whistled his way towards us with the cement in his wheelbarrow. He was powerfully built with broad shoulders, a professional beer-gut and a generally happy countenance.

'How's it going?' Frank Boston asked, as he drew close to us.

'Not bad, Mr Boston. Couple more days at the most.'

'Good, good,' Frank Boston replied, reaching inside his jacket and pulling out a leather cigar case. 'Have a cigar, Steve.'

'Oh, ta very much, Mr Boston,' the unsuspecting labourer said, helping himself to an expensive-looking smoke. 'I'll stick it behind me ear an' 'ave it later if it's all the same to you, thanks.'

'Smoke it,' Frank Boston replied, coldly, producing a gold Dunhill lighter and lighting it under the man's nose.

'What?'

'Smoke it.'

'What . . . like . . . now . . . you mean?'

'Yes, Steven – now.'

'Well . . . like . . . I'd rather, like . . . save it till . . .'

'Now!'

The unfortunate man's face was an animated catalogue of expressions of despair. He was hopelessly cornered but you could see that he was still going to

44

brazen it out. He raised the cigar to his lips, hesitated, then like a man swallowing hemlock he closed his eyes as he placed the cigar between his teeth.

'You'd better take the end off, Stevie,' Frank Boston said, 'otherwise it won't work, will it?'

'What?'

'You've forgotten the little cap of tobacco leaf over the end of the cigar, Steven. I'm surprised that a seasoned cigar connoisseur like you would forget that. Just snap it off with your finger nails – you don't need a cutter.'

I looked away as the hapless, helpless labourer mutilated the end of the cigar with his big, blunt fingers. As he reluctantly replaced the frayed end in his mouth, Frank Boston raised the lighter again. The man sucked tentatively at the flame.

'Come along, Steven – big drag now, get the thing going, son, otherwise I'll be standing here with this lighter all afternoon.'

He did as he was told, puffing furiously to expel the smoke from his mouth as soon as he took it in.

'No, no, no, Steve. Savour it. Enjoy it. *Inhale* it.'

'I'd really rather . . . I mean . . . I'd rather just . . .'

'Inhale it!'

He inhaled, spluttered, inhaled again, then turned away, doubling-up in a paroxysm of coughing, as big, wet tears rolled down his unshaven face. Frank Boston stood by impassively.

'Inhale,' he ordered again, at the first lull in his victim's suffering.

'But . . . Mr Bost . . .'

'Inhale!' Boston replied.

Amazingly, the tormented man did as instructed. But, this time, the re-doubled hacking and a now fast-developing pallor seemed to satisfy his torturer. Frank Boston took the tattered cigar from between the labourer's fingers, dropped it on the ground and trod it into the red tarmac.

'I'll see you between four-thirty and five then, Mr Harton,' he said, walking over to his Rolls Royce. It was as though the events of the last few minutes had never taken place.

As he drove off, I decided to slip away quietly myself. The unfortunate labourer was still bent double, retching as he clung with whitened knuckles to one of the columns of the portico. I felt that anything I might say would be received less than favourably, so I threw my briefcase into the Mini and clambered in.

Although the brief glimmer of warning lights and the dull clunk from under the bonnet were not entirely unexpected, I had hoped for better things. I got out of the car and looked over towards the broken figure, now on his knees by the front door. It seemed neither the time nor the place, but there was nothing else for it.

'Excuse me!' I called. 'I wonder if you would be kind enough to give me a push – my car doesn't seem too well.'

Charlotte was on the telephone when I burst, red-faced, into the office. 'Ah, hold on a moment,' she said, 'I think I can hear him coming now.'

'Who is it?' I mouthed, silently, still panting from having scaled the stairs two at a time.

She placed her hand over the receiver. 'It's Patrick Faulkner – something about vetting an antiques fair.'

'I'm in a hell of a rush. Tell him I'll call him back as soon as possible.'

'Er, hello, Patrick,' Charlotte said, 'I'm sorry, it wasn't Richard after all. Can I get him to ring you back when he gets in? ... all right ... yes ... I'll tell him ... goodbye.' She screwed up her face as she replaced the phone. 'Disgusting old lech,' she said.

'What did he want, anyway?' I asked.

'Like I said: something about vetting an antiques fair. He kept saying it was money for old rope.'

'Okay, I'll ring him later, when I get a minute. Any luck with the flat?'

'God! Don't even talk about it. You owe me an absolutely huge drink for what I've done for you there – well beyond the call of duty.'

'Why? What happened?'

'I've got an appointment for six o'clock this evening.'

'That's going to be tight. I don't know if I'll be able to . . .'

'Don't you dare say you can't make it,' Charlotte interrupted, glaring at me. 'It took me three-quarters of an hour this morning before I got through. Then I had to practically grovel to get her to see you. She'd had so many enquiries she wasn't going to see any more people, but I managed to persuade her to make an exception in your case.'

'Well done, but who exactly is "she"?'

'A Lady Barnes. I don't know where the title comes from but she sounds American. She was very nice but she clearly doesn't have a clue about letting flats and she's been completely overwhelmed by the number of people after hers. By the time I eventually got through to her she'd given up and was just turning people away.'

'How did you manage to convince her that she should see me?'

'It's a long story, but you do have quite a lot to live up to – and then there's your deprived childhood, the orphanage, juvenile court and so on.'

'I trust you are joking.'

'Yes, but I did mean it when I said don't you dare tell me you can't keep the appointment. After all the trouble I've had getting you in there, I'll quit if you cancel now.'

'No, all right, I'll get there somehow,' I assured her. 'It's just that, at the moment, I'm not quite sure how.'

Philip Lawrence, the manager of the Silver and Jewellery Department, had joined Hampson's a little over a year before I had. At thirty years of age he was much nearer to being my contemporary than any of the other departmental heads, and since, like me, he was just a manager while the others were directors, we quickly found that this gave us a common perspective when it came to company matters.

However, it wasn't company policy I wanted his views on that afternoon. It was Frank Boston's gemstone I needed him to look at, and quickly.

'I'm afraid Philip's out,' Miles Johnson, his assistant, informed me when I arrived at the Silver reception desk. 'He's due back any moment but then he's got to go straight out on another call. Can I help you?'

'I don't know – I've got a ring I need him to look at urgently.'

'Can I see it?'

I handed him the little draw-string bag and followed him into the office where he examined the stone under an eye-glass.

'What's it supposed to be?' he asked.

'A diamond.'

'Looks like a topaz to me,' he said, checking it once more.

'That's what I thought,' I replied, 'but I need to know for sure by four o'clock at the latest.'

'No problem. Leave it with me and I'll make sure the boss-man looks at it when he comes in. Is it for sale?'

'No, just for authentication.'

'Right.' Miles jotted down the details in a notebook, tore out the page and put it with the ring in the office safe. 'Fear not. It shall be done,' he said. 'In fact, there's another ring in for authentication so I'll get him to look at them both at the same time – that should concentrate his mind.'

'Good, give me a buzz as soon as he's looked at mine. I've got to get back to the owner post-haste.'

Although the main staircase at Hampson's was at least

six feet wide, the formidable figure of Patrick Faulkner seemed to overpower it, reducing its proportions to those of the most humble spiral staircase. It was evident that I was going to have to postpone my return to the Valuations Office until he'd unburdened himself of whatever it was he wanted to tell me.

'Richard! My dear boy! I've been trying to contact you all afternoon, but the ever delightful Miss Morrison maintained you were missing behind enemy lines.' He beamed genially as he spoke, but his eyes, a little puffier than usual, wandered all around never once making contact with my own.

'She was right, Patrick,' I said. 'I've only just got back, and I'm afraid I've got to rush out again in a minute, and my car's playing up and . . .'

'My dear chap, you really must slow down or you'll never see forty. Pace yourself. Pace yourself. Life should be sipped and savoured like a fine claret, not gulped down and belched back like a pint of rancid ale.' He stopped and smiled. 'I say, that was rather a good analogy, wasn't it? I must remember that one: fine claret and rancid ale.'

'Yes, Patrick, very good, but I really am up against it this afternoon . . .'

'Absolutely!' he said, taking me by the arm and manoeuvring me sideways to make room for one of the girls on her way downstairs from the Accounts Department to get past. I noticed that in getting me out of the way, he managed to place himself directly in her path. She side-stepped and just managed to slip between the wall and the now slightly perspiring Director of Furniture.

'I'm sorry, Sharon,' he called after her, as she skipped on down, 'so clumsy of me.'

'Patrick,' I remarked, to the back of his head, while he watched the retreating Sharon White, 'I really do have to dash. If this is going to take long . . .'

'No, no, Richard,' he said, temporarily returning his attention to me, 'it won't take a moment. It's just about the Dereford Antiques Fair – I don't suppose you've ever heard of it?'

'No, I can't say I have.'

'No, well, no reason why you should have. It's quite a small concern. You know the sort of thing: held in the village hall, rain drumming on the galvanised tin roof, windows misted up with the steam produced by the witches' brew in the tea urn, floor-boards creaking like arthritic hips . . .'

'I think I've got the picture,' I interrupted.

'Yes, of course, I forgot, you're in a rush. Sorry, dear boy . . . ' he paused, strategically re-deploying his bulk as Sharon White approached us on her way back upstairs. She looked to his right, selling him the perfect dummy as at the very last minute she side-stepped to his left. In an instant she was between us and gone, leaving just her heavy musk perfume lingering on the air to confirm that she had indeed passed that way. Patrick Faulkner gazed after her with the respectful smile of a hunter deprived of a kill by the superior cunning of his prey.

'Patrick, I really do have to go!'

'Yes, yes, Richard. I won't keep you a moment. As I was saying, they have about forty stalls, no pictures, the dateline is 1860, and Hampson's vet it every year. In the past I've always gone down with Bernard Thornton doing porcelain, and Douglas Boyd, Philip Lawrence's predecessor, covering silver and jewellery. This year, as luck would have it, I'm going to be away and Bernard's not able to make it either. So, I've got young Lawrence lined up for the silver, and Bernard's arranged for his assistant, William Baron, to stand in for him. All we need now is someone for furniture and clocks. What about it, Richard?'

'As long as I haven't got anything else on.'

'Excellent! It's all set up for Thursday evening. Dereford's just this side of Oxford. My advice is: give the traffic time to clear, then shoot off down there; give the place the once-over, reject anything post 1860 – there's not likely to be more than a couple of pieces; collect the cash and retire to the pub over the road for a damn good supper.'

'Cash?'

'Yes, old chap, cash. That's why I don't want to let them down. They pay a fee of one hundred and twenty green ones for our impartial expertise. No Hampson's bills or messy paperwork. No income tax or VAT. Just good, old-fashioned cash in the outstretched, sticky palm. Forty pounds per man. I'd hate them to take their custom elsewhere. Anyway, I can ink you in then? You'll do it?'

'Yes, I suppose so.'

'Good man! Young Lawrence has got all the details. Sort it out with him.'

Philip Lawrence's telephone rang several times before Miles Johnson answered it. 'Silver Department,' he sighed.

'It's Richard here, Miles. Are you having problems?'

'Yes! I've had the world and his wife in here this afternoon since you came up. It would be the one afternoon that I'm on my own.'

'Has Philip looked at the ring?' I asked.

'Yes, but I didn't have a chance to talk to him about it. There's a note here somewhere. Hold on, I'll find it . . .'

'Don't worry,' I said, 'I'll come over. I've got to get the ring back to its owner straight away – it's already gone four. I'll come up now and collect it and you can tell me about it then.'

It came as no surprise when Miles gave me the verdict: 'According to this illegible scrawl,' he said, peering at the tattered piece of paper, and handing me the little draw-string bag, 'the contents of this bag would not cut ice, let alone glass.'

'Oh, dear.'

'Anything else I can do for you, Richard, before I self-destruct?'

'Yes, if I'm not back by six o'clock, perhaps you'd be kind enough to start dragging the Thames.'

It was almost ten minutes to five, and dark by the time I once again drew up on the red tarmac in front of Mr Boston's overgrown porch. At least, it was dark elsewhere in the South-East. Frank Boston's house and garden were lit up like Wembley stadium on a match night. Under the glare of the brilliant floodlights I noticed with some interest that, although the Rolls was back in position outside the garage, the Mercedes was still absent. It appeared that Susie and Trish were still gossiping.

'Hello, Mr Harton. What's the verdict?' Frank Boston asked, before I'd even stepped across the threshold.

'Well,' I said, bracing myself, 'I don't think you're going to like what . . .'

I was interrupted by the trilling of a telephone.

'Hold on a second,' my client instructed, 'I'll just get that.' He went into the drawing room, returning just a few moments later. 'It's for you,' he said. 'Your secretary I think. She wants a word.' He showed me into the drawing room and gestured to an onyx and ormolu telephone which I had earlier toyed with listing under the Objets D'Art heading in his inventory. It came as a bit of a disappointment to find that it was actually functional. It was the sort of thing that might just as easily have turned out to be a novelty cigar lighter or an executive toy.

I picked it up and pressed the unwieldy instrument to my ear.

'Hello,' I said.

'Richard, it's Charlotte. Can you talk?'

'No.'

'Is Mr Boston in the room with you?'

'Yes.'

'Okay, listen carefully.'

'Right.'

'Have you told him the ring's no good.'

'No.'

'Thank goodness for that. I've just had Philip Lawrence on in a great state. Apparently there was another ring in for authentication this afternoon.'

'Yes.'

'Well, Miles muddled up the notes somehow. It was the other ring that was no good. The one you brought in was kosher. Philip says he can understand why you had your doubts but the chipping and scratching isn't that unusual, and there's absolutely nothing wrong with it. He says it's worth a lot of money.'

'Right.'

'Okay, I'll leave you to break the good news, and you have remembered you've got an appointment with Lady Barnes at six o'clock, haven't you?'

'Yes.'

'Good. Bye, bye, then.'

'Bye,' I said, replacing the receiver.

'You're a man after my own heart,' my client remarked.

'Sorry?' I replied, trying to remember just how far I'd actually gone towards telling Frank Boston that his whacking great, highly valuable diamond was definitely a relatively worthless topaz.

'You're a man of few words, Mr Harton. On the telephone, there: about the only things you said were, yes and no. That's the way to handle staff – short, sharp and decisive.'

'Yes, quite,' I said, almost certain that I'd been in the middle of explaining to my client that he wasn't going to like what I was about to tell him.

'Anyway,' he went on, 'I take it the news on the ring isn't good.'

'Ah . . . the ring . . . no, on the contrary, the news on the ring is excellent. Our jewellery specialist has given it a clean bill of health. It's very definitely a diamond.'

'Good. I'm glad about that, Mr Harton. I really would have been very upset if it hadn't passed muster. I've known the bloke who gave it to me for a long time.' As he spoke he withdrew his cigar case from his jacket pocket. 'But, if the ring's all right, what was it you were talking about when you said I wasn't going to like what you had to say?'

'Er . . . oh, that . . . well, it's just that I'm having trouble with my car and I'm afraid I'm going to have to ask if you'd mind giving me a push, Mr Boston.' It was the best I could manage under the circumstances.

'Is that all? I thought it was something serious! No, I don't mind.' He went to put his cigar case away, hesitated, then held it out to me. 'Here, Mr Harton, have a cigar.'

Before I could answer, and for the first time since I'd met him earlier that day, his face creased into a broad, toothy smile.

'You don't have to smoke it now, you know,' he said. 'You can always stick it behind your ear for later.'

It was six o'clock on the dot when I parked in Gladstone Road, W8, just opposite number fourteen. It was a handsome town house, tall and elegant, though not huge.

The door was opened by a relieved-looking, grey-haired woman wearing a warm winter coat and a headscarf.

'Mr Harton?' she asked, her accent still rooted in New England. 'Thank goodness I got back in time! I just *had* to take the dog for a walk. The poor old thing hadn't been out all day. Then I found my watch had stopped

54

and I didn't know what time it was, or whether you might have been and gone, so I came rushing back here, and I've just made it. Phew!' She took a deep breath and smiled a big friendly smile. 'I'm Dorothy Barnes. Come on in.'

Once inside, she took off her scarf and coat and tossed them over the bannister rail, then banished Max, a somewhat overweight and superannuated black labrador, to the kitchen.

'Right!' she said. 'Let's go up and have a look at this bijou little *pied-à-terre*. I hope you're not expecting too much, Mr Harton, because I can assure you, too much it ain't.'

Slowly, we trudged up three floors.

'After the number of times I've climbed these stairs today,' she said, 'I don't mind if I never visit this flat again.'

It turned out to be small and self-contained with one good-sized bedroom. It was basic, old-fashioned and a little bit cold. It was also the sort of place for which, at twenty-five pounds a week, I would have been prepared to fight to the death.

'And it's a little bit chilly I'm afraid,' Lady Barnes said, concluding her exhaustive list of its faults. 'It's on the main central heating system but, by the time it gets up this far, the water's only tepid at best. The hot water for the bathroom's fine though, and the kitchen's got its own geyser.'

'What about gas, electricity and telephone?' I asked.

'They're all the same as the rest of the house. The rent's inclusive of all bills like that.

Back downstairs in the dining room, Dorothy Barnes rummaged about in the drinks cupboard. 'How about whisky and water?' she asked. 'I can generally pour that without making a mess of it.'

Although the previous evening's excesses had rather impaired my taste for scotch, after the day I'd had I

55

needed something. 'That would be fine,' I replied, 'only, just a small one with lots of water, please.'

I watched as she dispensed the drinks. Despite her face being a picture of intense concentration, I got nearly half a tumbler of whisky and about the same of water.

'Now,' she said, as we settled into old armchairs on either side of the fireplace, 'are you interested in the flat?'

'Yes, Lady Barnes . . .'

'Oh, please don't call me that,' she interrupted. 'I'm just a simple colonial girl who, many years ago, fell in love with a clever young English doctor. Because of the ridiculous, archaic conventions that still abound in this funny old country he, one day, suddenly became *Sir* Gerald Barnes. But, I don't see why I have to go along with all that nonsense too; just plain Dorothy is still good enough for me.'

'All right,' I said. 'In that case, I think you'd better call me Richard, rather than Mr Harton.'

'It's a deal.'

'And, in answer to your question,' I went on, 'yes, I would very much like to take your flat. It would be absolutely ideal.'

'Okay – now that leaves me with a problem.'

'What's that?'

'I've already promised it to someone else.'

My heart fell. It would have been too much to hope that I'd be the only person who would be interested in taking the place. But I had assumed that she would have delayed making the decision until she'd seen the last applicant.

'We've never let it before,' she continued, 'and I decided from the outset that I'd only let it to someone who really needed it.'

I began to think that Charlotte actually should have created a history of orphanages and juvenile crime for me.

'The person I've promised it to is a young woman who has had a very bad time of it, and all in all I think you'd probably find it easier to get another flat than she would.'

'I see,' I said, glumly.

'But, I am insisting she lets me have references, and if they're not up to scratch, as far as I'm concerned the place is yours if you still want it by then. Your secretary explained how desperate you are for a place so I know you qualify as needy.' She paused, took a sip of the fire-water she held in her hand, screwed up her face and coughed. 'I've done it again – why do I always make it so strong?' she said. 'Incidentally, you should give that girl an immediate pay-rise – she did a really great sales job for you.'

'Yes, she suggested as much to me,' I replied.

'Okay,' she went on, standing up and putting her glass on the mantleshelf. 'Now, would you like me to contact you if this female doesn't come up with the goods? It's an outside chance I know, but you never can tell.'

'Yes, please,' I said, rather huskily, having just gulped down the incendiary contents of my own glass.

'All right, Richard. I'll let you know one way or the other just as soon as I can.'

I arrived back at Tom Morrison's place tired and dispirited. Of course, the car had refused to start again when I went to leave Gladstone Road, but it was the flat that had really upset me. To have so narrowly missed it was much worse than not being in the running at all. And it had been perfect: quiet, ideally placed, and all my own. Sharing was all very well, but I wasn't designed to enjoy co-habiting with three or four lunatic males. I needed a bit of space and occasionally a bit of peace.

As I turned the key in the lock and opened the front door I was assailed by an amazing barrage of noise.

Somehow, Tom managed to lift his voice above the deep, booming bass and the whining, jagged howl of guitars, 'RICHARD! NO SKULKING-OFF TO YOUR ROOM. IT'S PARTY TIME!'

Chapter 5

'Where have you been?' Charlotte asked. 'Bob Derby wants to see you.'

'Well, he can wait,' I said, hanging up my overcoat. 'I'm not doing anything until I've had a cup of coffee.'

'Something tells me we're not in the best of moods this morning.'

'Full marks for observation,' I said, sitting down at my desk to go through the morning's meagre selection of mail.

'Tell Aunty Charlotte all about it.'

'To start with, it took me half an hour to get the car started again this morning.'

'I thought it was supposed to be in the garage today.'

'It is now, but I did have to get it there, Charlotte.'

'Oh, that's a point, I suppose,' she acknowledged. 'So that explains why you're late. But something else is bugging you – Aunty can tell.'

'Aunty's quite right – I didn't get the flat. Lady Barnes had already let it by the time I got there.'

'What! But she promised she wouldn't do anything until you'd seen it. The old bat!'

'Funnily enough, that's one thing she's not,' I said, screwing up the first of the letters and tossing it at the wastepaper basket. It hit the rim and rolled across the floor towards Charlotte's desk.

'That was a dreadful shot,' Charlotte observed, as she munched away at her occasional breakfast treat, a bacon sandwich. 'But why do you say she's not an old bat?'

'Because I think she genuinely let the place to the person concerned because she felt sorry for her.' I fired off the next three letters in quick succession in the general direction of the bin. 'She's a nice lady,' I concluded.

'If you say so,' Charlotte mumbled, her mouth full of bacon butty.

'I do, but it is a shame. The place was perfect.' I screwed the last letter into a small, tight ball, aimed it carefully at the waste bin and sent it on its way. In common with the first missile it hit the rim. Then it bounced onto the floor and rolled across the carpet, stopping just inside the door at the feet of the Chairman of Hampson's.

Robert Derby was a big, dark, strongly built man of about forty-five to fifty years of age. Well dressed and expensively tanned, he had a considerable physical presence, especially when you weren't expecting him to be there in the first place.

'Interesting filing system, Richard,' he said, kicking the piece of paper back across the office towards the bin. 'I suppose it cuts down on cabinets.'

To suggest that this sudden appearance in the office took us by surprise would be to seriously understate the case. Until then, as far as we knew, all visitors had to buzz us on the street door security phone before they could get in. Neither of us had any idea that he had his own key, nor had we heard him coming up the stairs. So, our behaviour on his arrival was far from composed.

While Charlotte swept her bacon sandwich into the top drawer of her desk and snatched up a pen, I jumped out of my chair to greet him, almost removing a kneecap on the side of my desk as I did so.

Derby stepped forward, smiling, hand outstretched. His walk was a little reminiscent of a boxer advancing in the ring – shoulders slightly hunched, face thrust pugnaciously forward. He was a man to reckon with.

'You'd better sit down before you fall down, Richard,' he said. 'That was a nasty blow by the sound of it.'

I smiled weakly and slid back into my seat.

'And do take your breakfast out of the drawer, Charlotte. It'll make the most awful mess of the stationery.' He pulled up a chair and sat down. 'And I think you'll find that pen will work more efficiently if you hold it the right way up,' he went on without even casting a glance in my secretary's direction.

She looked down at the inverted ballpen in her hand, closed her eyes and shook her head despairingly.

'So, how's it going, Richard?' our visitor asked. 'Settling in all right?'

'Yes, fine,' I replied. 'Of course, I'm still just beginning to find my way around.'

'Oh, of course. It's bound to take a while, especially having come from a small set-up. I expect you're finding everything rather different.'

'Yes.'

'Well, you're bound to. Have you met everybody?'

'Most of them, I think,' I replied, still massaging my knee under the desk.

'Charles Morrison-Whyte? Bernard Thornton? Patrick Faulkner?'

'I've not met Bernard Thornton yet. I think he's away.'

'Oh, yes. I believe he's off skiing somewhere – a bit cold at this time of the year for me. But, there you are, Bernard's a bit of a maniac. Do you ski?'

'No.'

'You should – best holiday there is. Mind you, I don't think I'll get away this year. My wife insisted on sunshine at Christmas instead. Have you got a flat yet?'

'Only temporary. I've just missed a good one.'

'Never mind, you'll land one sooner or later. How's the car running?'

'The battery's died. It's in dock today being fixed.'

61

'That's a nuisance. You'll have to borrow one of the other cars. I want you to go down to Kent.'

'When?'

'Now. You haven't anything in your diary have you?'

'No, but . . .'

'Good, I've promised the Mother Superior of the Convent of Saint Ursula that you'll be with her by eleven o'clock,' he said, adding in a pious tone, 'God willing.'

'I see,' I said. 'What's it all about?'

'Well, as you are doubtless aware, Saint Ursula, a virgin martyr of the first order, is the patron saint of young girls and women engaged in the education of their own sex.'

'Of course.'

'Yes, I felt sure you'd know that,' he continued. 'Now, the good Reverend Mother's decided that it's no longer acceptable for a couple of dozen elderly nuns to go on indefinitely, rattling around inside some ghastly Victorian pile which they can't afford to heat let alone maintain . . .'

'Good for her,' Charlotte said, without looking up.

'Quite,' agreed Bob Derby, giving her a sidelong glance. 'So the Church is flogging the property to a developer, buying smaller premises and opening a brand new school.'

'And the Mother Superior wants us to look at the contents?' I said.

'That's about the size of it,' he replied. 'I have no idea what's there, but you never know. By the way, I told the good lady I was sending our ecclesiastical specialist.'

'Thanks very much.'

'That's all right – only joking.' He got up and replaced his chair in its original position. 'While I think of it, Richard, pop in and see me some time. I want to talk to you about organising some lunches in our boardroom for small groups of solicitors. I think it'll help to get the probate valuation side going.'

'Okay,' I said, 'but we could do with some advertising

on the insurance side as well.'

'Mmmm,' he murmured, looking doubtful. 'Well, we can talk about it, but don't get your hopes up. Good luck with Saint Ursula. Bye-bye, Charlotte.'

Neither Charlotte nor I spoke until some time after we had heard the street door slam.

'God! I hate it when he does that,' she moaned. 'There's something about the man – he always makes me behave like a complete moron. I mean, just look at me – trying to hide my bacon sandwich like some schoolgirl caught having a midnight feast in the dorm. It's so pathetic! He makes me feel guilty even when I haven't done anything.'

'I didn't even know he had a key,' I said.

'Nor did I. I thought I'd got away from his little surprise visits when I moved into this office. He does it all the time next door, of course.'

'Really?'

'Oh, yes. He once walked in when I was imitating how Charles Morrison-Whyte speaks when he's on the rostrum – all adenoidal and clipped vowels. The first I knew about him being there was when he applauded and said, 'Bravo!' I nearly died.'

'Well, I hope he doesn't make a habit of it here. It makes for an unnerving start to the day,' I said, finishing off the last dregs of cold coffee in my cup. 'Now, Charlotte – a little job for you.'

'What's that?'

'Find me a motorcar. I have to leave for Kent in approximately five minutes.'

Robert Derby was right: the Convent of Saint Ursula was a ghastly Victorian pile. Even in its heyday it could never have looked beautiful, but now it looked downright disreputable. Its red brick needed re-pointing, its stonework was flaking, and its slate roof looked as though it was very probably leaking.

63

However, it stood in the middle of a sizeable plot, in an otherwise fully developed residential road, on the edge of a tacky suburban sprawl. No doubt it was worth a fortune.

While driving down, I'd thought a lot about just how I should deal with the Reverend Mother. After all, she was unlikely to be particularly well versed in the ways of commerce, and she would almost certainly be upset at having to preside over the break-up of the old convent.

Poor protestant fool that I was, I had a lot to learn about the Mother Superior of Saint Ursula's. And the lessons started the moment I arrived.

'To begin with, Mr Harton,' she said, as I sprinted along beside her, 'we have no time to lose.'

'Right, Mother Superior.'

'We got a particularly good price on the land deal because we were prepared to complete in a hurry – we've only got three weeks to go – so I'm grateful to you for coming down at such short notice. Of course, we've asked a local auctioneer to cast his eye over what we've got, as well.'

'Right.'

'There's absolutely no point in our paying removal charges for taking things to London if they'll sell better in the local rooms anyway – don't you agree?'

'Absolutely, Mother Superior.'

'Now, as far as I'm concerned, everything in this building is for sale. Whether we sell or not depends on just one thing: what you think the items will make.'

'I understand.'

'Every penny we raise will go towards equipping the new school, but things like beds and so on can, to some extent, be accommodated in the living quarters of the new building.'

'Yes.'

'We may as well start with the upper floors,' she continued, as we began to ascend a dark, musty back

64

staircase. 'I doubt there'll be anything to interest you up there, but you'd better look it over just the same.'

'Quite, Mother Superior.'

Taking the stairs two at a time to keep up with her, it struck me that the Catholic Church's gain was British Industry's loss. The Mother Superior of the Convent of Saint Ursula would have made a formidable company chairman.

'Have you any questions, Mr Harton?' she asked, as we skipped up the last flight of stairs.

'Yes – what about the sisters' private property?'

'They have no private property. Our order regards all property as being communally owned.' She turned as we attained the top floor landing. 'As I said, *everything* here is for sale.'

During my pursuit of the Mother Superior through the gloomy, rambling building, I'd observed feverish activity amongst its other inmates. Bob Derby may well have been right about there being only a couple of dozen nuns in residence, but there seemed to be a great many more. Dashing to and fro, laden with boxes, packing cases and even pieces of furniture, they were obviously engaged in a full-scale evacuation.

'The more items we pack and carry to the ground floor ourselves, the less our removal bill will be,' the Reverend Mother explained when I commented on the general level of animation. I wondered which company had been unlucky enough to win the contract for the move. Whichever it was, it was a foregone conclusion that the profit margin would be very slim.

'That's a nice chair,' I said, selecting a handsome George I dining chair from a line of less aristocratic examples in one of the upper dormitories. 'We can take that. It should make three to four hundred pounds.'

'Good,' replied my guide. 'Is there anything else in here of interest to Hampson's, Mr Harton?'

'No, not really,' I replied, taking one last look around

the room with its rows of old beds and lino-covered floor. 'Everything else will sell just as well, if not better, locally.'

'Right,' she said, already heading for the stairs. 'Let's go down to the next floor.'

Exhausted-looking nuns, ascending the stairs for the umpteenth time that morning, jumped aside as the Mother Superior and I clattered down again.

It was about twenty minutes later, in a small room off one of the large dormitories on the first floor that I spotted it.

'Oh, look at that,' I said. 'That's a bonus.'

'What, Mr Harton?'

'There, in that stack.' I pointed to a pile of furniture by the window. 'Unless I'm very much mistaken, that's the pair to the George I chair we saw upstairs.'

'Do you think so?'

I quickly dismantled the stack and retrieved the chair. The most cursory inspection confirmed it: it was identical to the one on the top floor.

'Well, that's excellent news,' I said. 'As I mentioned earlier, on its own, a chair like that's worth three to four hundred pounds. But a pair's a different matter altogether. I would expect a pair to make a thousand to twelve hundred pounds.'

'Well, that *is* good news,' beamed the Reverend Mother. 'I wonder if we'll find any more.'

As the morning went on, I began to recognise individual nuns as they crossed and re-crossed my path, sometimes staggering along with full loads, sometimes dragging their weary way back for the next consignment. One in particular caught my eye. She looked fairly elderly, was slightly lame and also a little bit nervous and mouse-like, scampering past me as fast as she could whenever we met. Most noticeably, one of the items she carried was always the same. It looked to be some sort of workbox, but I never got a chance to see it

66

clearly because, each time, it was either half-buried among the other things she was carrying or just partly hidden under her robes. Whatever it was, she wasn't letting it out of her sight. Unfortunately for her, I wasn't the only one to have noticed.

'Sister Agnes!' the Reverend Mother addressed the furtive nun in ringing tones.

'Er . . . yes . . . Mother?' Her reply was faltering but her facial expression was one of beatific innocence.

'Let Mr Harton see your box, Sister.'

'My . . . er . . . my . . . er . . . box, Mother?'

'Yes, your box, Sister.' The Reverend Mother towered over her charge as she spoke to her. 'Quickly now, Mr Harton's in a hurry.'

Slowly, and with ill-disguised reluctance, Sister Agnes produced an early nineteenth-century Tunbridge-ware workbox. I examined it with care. A few small pieces of veneer were missing and one hinge had been wrenched back at some stage, splitting the back of the box slightly. Apart from that, it was in excellent condition and highly saleable.

'Is it worth anything, Mr Harton?' the Mother Superior asked.

As I looked up to give her my answer, my eyes met those of Sister Agnes. They were the most expressive eyes I'd ever seen. They were begging, pleading, imploring me to say the box was worthless. What was more, she looked old, desperately old, worn out and hopeless. But she said nothing. She just stood there, with her hands lightly clasped in front of her, waiting for my *coup de grâce*. Waiting to lose her treasure.

'Er . . . unfortunately not,' I heard myself say, as I handed the box back to Sister Agnes.

'Really?' There was a definite note of suspicion in the Reverend Mother's voice.

I hesitated. Of course, if the local auctioneer had seen it, he would already have told her it was worth several hundred pounds. If that was the case, and I still tried to keep up this little charade, not only was I going to lose the sale of the workbox, I was also going to look a complete idiot.

'I'm afraid so,' I said, abandoning my fate to the prayers of Sister Agnes. 'It's the damage, you see.'

'But it is Tunbridge-ware, isn't it?'

That confirmed it beyond any doubt – the other auctioneer must have told her what it was really worth. There was nothing else for it now, I just had to brazen it out.

'Oh, yes, it's Tunbridge-ware,' I said, 'but the missing veneer . . . the split back . . . the fading colours . . . and of course it's a *terribly* late example.'

'Oh, I wouldn't dispute that it's nineteenth century rather than eighteenth century,' the lady said, 'but I rather thought it might be the work of Robert Russell.'

Robert Russell! Oh, no! She knew about Robert Russell – the man who exhibited a lady's Tunbridge-ware workbox at the Great Exhibition. She knew about him! What was the point of going on? She knew more about it than I did! I was dead meat!

'No, no,' I said, as I felt my smile begin to develop a nervous tic, 'no, it's not Russell's work . . . although I can understand why you thought it might be . . . although it's not . . . of course . . .' It was getting worse. I'd already shot myself in both feet. Another word and I'd probably blow my brains out.

There was a long pause, then the Reverend Mother smiled at the guardian of the Tunbridge-ware box. 'Well, Sister Agnes, it would seem that you can indeed keep your workbox. Mr Harton confirms what our other auctioneer told us – it's too damaged to be of any value.'

As I once more trailed along beside the Mother Superior, across the landing and down the main stairs, I reflected on what an extraordinary woman she was, and wondered if she had really swallowed the story about the workbox, even if it had come from two unrelated expert witnesses.

'Are you a Catholic, Mr Harton?' she asked, as we descended to the front hall.

'No, Mother. I'm an Anglican.'

'Never mind, you're a good man,' she said, 'even if you are an appalling liar.'

'I don't know what you mean, Mother Superior.'

She turned and smiled as we reached the bottom of the stairs. 'Of course you don't, Mr Harton. But, then, I'm beginning to believe that all auctioneers are as innocent as babes in arms. Now, where shall we start down here?'

It was some time later, in the refectory, that I spotted the third chair.

'I don't believe it,' I said. 'It's another of those George I chairs. I wonder if there's a fourth somewhere. That would really make them worth some money.'

'Are you sure it's part of the same set, Mr Harton?'

'Absolutely,' I said, bending down to examine it properly. 'Look, Mother – exactly the same shaped back; the same delightful little shell motif on the knee of the cabriole; the same pad-foot . . . the same little repair on the cresting rail ?'

'Oh, dear, Mr Harton. Are you thinking what I'm thinking?'

'I'm trying not to, Mother, but . . .'

'Sister Catherine,' the Reverend Mother called to a nun who had just stumbled into the room with a tea chest, 'how long has this chair been in the refectory?'

'That one?' replied the puce-faced, puffing sister. 'About ten minutes, I think, Mother. Sister Magaret brought it down from upstairs.'

The Mother Superior strode from the refectory and through the hall to the foot of the stairs. 'SISTER MARGARET!' she bellowed, in a voice that would have struck fear into the heart of the most recalcitrant guardsman.

'Yes, Mother,' came the faint reply.

'Come here, please!'

Somewhere high above us, somebody started to run. I heard the feet pound down one staircase, across the bare boards of a landing, then down another set of stairs. Louder and louder it got until, eventually, Sister Margaret hove into view, galloping down the main staircase to where the Mother Superior stood. Like Sister Catherine, she was red in the face and panting.

'Yes, Mother,' she said, a little nervously.

'Sister, have you just brought a chair downstairs? An old one, with little shells carved on the front legs?'

'Er . . . yes, Mother.'

'Where did you get it from, Sister?'

'It was in one of the little rooms up there.' She pointed towards the floor above.

The Mother Superior gave me a resigned look. 'And how did it get there?' she asked the still panting sister.

'Oh, Sister Elizabeth brought it down from the top floor earlier this morning,' she said, brightly.

It was almost three o'clock when the Reverend Mother escorted me to my car.

'I hope it hasn't been a wasted trip for you, Mr Harton,' she said, as I put my briefcase in the car.

'Not at all,' I replied, 'I'm sure the pieces I've selected will sell very well at Hampson's.'

'Good! As long as you feel it's been worthwhile.'

'Oh, I do. Mind you, it's a pity about the incredible shrinking set of chairs.'

She laughed. 'Never mind, Mr Harton. I'll offer up a prayer to Saint Lucy for you tonight. She'll help you with your chairs and workboxes in future, I'm sure.'

'Why? Don't tell me she's the patron saint of auctioneers.'

'No, she takes care of people with eye problems.'

70

Chapter 6

William Baron was already waiting by the car when Philip Lawrence and I arrived. In the short time I'd been at Hampson's I hadn't had much opportunity to get to know him, but whenever our paths had crossed he'd struck me as quiet, efficient and helpful.

'I hope you haven't been waiting long, William,' Philip said, as he unlocked his car.

'No,' he replied, 'I've only just got here myself.'

'Good. Now, I'm afraid that on the grounds of seniority and due to the fact that you're six inches shorter than Richard, you get the back seat. You'll find it extremely uncomfortable and you'll probably have to dangle your legs out of the window, but that's life.'

'I don't care what it's like,' he said, clambering into the back of the car, 'as long as I'm out of this rain.'

'Right,' Philip said, as we did up our seat belts, 'Dereford here we come.'

The rain continued to fall steadily as we drove out of London onto the M40, and then on towards Oxford. I didn't envy the driver. The combination of headlights reflecting back off the wet road, filthy spray being thrown up by the heavy vehicles around us, and the sheer volume of water dropping from the heavens made conditions particularly bad. It was certainly not an ideal night for travelling.

'Anybody know what the Dereford Antiques Fair is like?' William Baron asked, after a while.

'Only what Patrick Faulkner told me,' I said. 'I believe it's reasonably modest.'

'What's the dateline?'

'1860, according to Patrick,' Philip said, 'but he was pretty vague about the whole thing.'

'Yes,' I said, 'the general impression he gave me was that it would take ten minutes to look the place over, then we could take the money and run.'

'Yes, that's more or less what he suggested to me,' Philip replied, narrowing his eyes as he peered into the night, 'but I think we should have a proper game plan. We should all be equally severe or equally lenient. There're always some marginal pieces at this sort of do.'

'Well, I suggest we play it strictly by the rulebook,' I said. 'If there's any doubt about an item, we reject it.'

'Sounds fair enough to me,' Philip agreed.

'Yes,' William Baron concurred, from behind us.

'Mind you, Richard,' Philip added, 'it's all very well for you to come down tough, it'll be William and I who have all the duff stuff to deal with – you see. With a dateline as late as 1860, you're not likely to get much dodgy furniture, are you?'

'I wouldn't have thought so,' I agreed brightly, 'but I will of course be only too happy to give you chaps the benefit of my opinion in your own areas should you require it.'

'I'll just drop him off here on the hard shoulder, shall I, William?' our driver asked.

'If you would, please,' replied the contorted figure in the back.

From the outside, Dereford Village Hall fitted almost exactly the picture so colourfully sketched by Patrick Faulkner. Although larger than I expected, it was otherwise a typical example of 1930s rural-civic architecture: part cheap over-baked brick, part creosoted weatherboard, all topped off with the regulation corrugated tin roof.

Avoiding the dozen or so estate cars and vans which littered the potholed car park, Philip parked as close as possible to the ramshackle porch which marked the entrance to the building. Although the rain was now the conventional vertical kind rather than the horizontal variety we had encountered on the motorway, we still lost no time in getting from the car to the building.

Inside, the porch was lined with rows of old-fashioned cast-iron coat hooks, some of which were draped with assorted wet weather gear that varied from the damp to the downright soaked. Pools of muddy water lay about the quarry-tiled floor. The atmosphere was cold, damp and uninviting.

'What a way to make a living,' Philip Lawrence muttered, as we combed our hair, straightened our ties and generally tried to make ourselves look vaguely presentable again.

'Think of the cash, men,' I comforted them. 'All set?'

'Yes, lead on, Skipper,' William Baron said, adding quietly under his breath: 'Let's get it over with.'

I pushed open the swing doors to the main hall and we stepped into the world of the Dereford Antiques Fair.

My first impression was that there just wasn't enough room for the three of us. Whoever had been responsible for allocating space couldn't be accused of failing to maximise returns. There were nearly forty stalls in an area better suited to twenty, but, if nothing else, the concentrated layout certainly gave an overall impression of activity, even without there being any members of the public present. Both sides of the room were lined with displays of furniture, porcelain and other decorative pieces, as was the wall behind us. A back to back row of stands down the centre of the hall appeared to be largely given over to ceramics, glass and bronzes, while the stage at the far end of the room was devoted to silver and jewellery.

Many of the stands were unattended, but quite a few were having the finishing touches put to them. I watched one woman as she stepped several paces backwards off her stand to get a better impression of an impressive Royal Worcester vase. She was obviously unhappy with it and stepped forward to give it a half turn. Stepping back again she put her head on one side, then walked to the other corner of her stand to view the piece from another angle. There was a moment's hesitation then she turned her attention to re-positioning a small occasional table. It seemed the vase was judged to be displayed to optimum effect.

'What a shame,' I remarked.

'Yes, especially after all that effort,' agreed William Baron, who like me had been watching the dealer's dedication to detail.

'Why?' Philip whispered. 'What's the problem?'

'About forty years, I would think,' I replied, quietly.

'What?' he said. 'You mean it's post-1860?'

'I mean it's post-1900,' I said.

'Almost certainly,' William added. 'That highland landscape with the soggy cattle is either going to be by Davis or Stinton, and both of them worked for Royal Worcester post-1900.'

'Oh, well,' Philip said, beaming at our colleague, 'at least you're going to earn your wages this evening, young William. I don't think the lady is going to respond too well to your news.'

'No,' I said, 'and she's at least a stone heavier than you, William.'

'Yes,' Philip went on, 'my advice is to use your feet, don't get in close, keep her at a distance with your left jab and keep bobbing and weaving.'

'Very funny,' William muttered. 'And I hope you both have an enjoyable evening as well.'

'Watch it, fellas,' Philip whispered, suddenly, 'we've been spotted. There's a businesslike lady approaching on your blind side, Richard.'

I turned to see a very attractive dark-haired woman bearing down on us. She wore an expensive-looking sheepskin coat, faded blue jeans and a harassed expression.

'Can I help you?' she asked, in a tone which suggested she couldn't.

'Yes,' I said, 'we're from Hampson's. I believe you're expecting us.'

'Oh, thank goodness,' she said, with obvious relief. 'It's such a disgusting night, I was beginning to wonder if you'd make it. I'm Julia Williams, the fair organiser.'

'Hello,' I said, 'I'm Richard Harton, and these are my colleagues, Philip Lawrence and William Baron.'

'Hello,' Julia Williams greeted my companions, 'I expect you want to get it over with as soon as possible, so don't let me hold you up. If there's anything you need, just give me a shout – I'll be up on the stage.'

'Fine,' I said.

'Oh, and by the way,' she added, drawing·closer and dropping her voice in a conspiratorial manner, 'who's going to be vetting the furniture?'

'I shall,' I answered, conscious of more than the faintest suggestion of trouble in her voice.

'Ah, Mr Harton. Well, I think it's only fair to warn you that you may have a little trouble with one of the stands.'

'What sort of trouble?' Philip asked, unable to contain either his curiosity or delight.

'Well, I'd rather not say,' Julia Williams replied. 'I think it's best if Mr Harton just makes up his own mind about it, if you see what I mean?'

I didn't, but I wasn't going to argue about it. As Philip Lawrence took the opportunity to escort the organiser back to the stage, William Baron and I split up and went about our business.

Generally speaking, the standard of the pieces on

show was surprisingly good. By the time I'd got two-thirds of the way around the hall I hadn't seen a single piece of furniture to argue about, whereas I'd spotted at least three pieces I would have liked to have owned. I glanced up at Philip Lawrence on the stage; he seemed to be deeply engrossed in conversation with Julia Williams. He was holding a spoon and was clearly discussing it in some detail. Mrs Williams, who was hanging on every word, moved closer to Philip to get a better look at the piece of silver as he turned it round to catch the light.

At precisely that moment, I encountered William coming in the opposite direction. 'Must be a very interesting spoon,' he muttered. 'Lawrence has been discussing its merits and demerits for getting on for ten minutes now.'

'That's nothing,' I said, 'I've seen him take twenty minutes over a plated meat cover. Of course, the owner was stunning.'

'Yes,' William replied, watching our comrade and his attentive one-woman audience, 'I suppose this little lecture's really got more to do with the recipient than it has the subject matter.'

I looked around the room again. 'Have you had to throw much out?' I asked. 'Only a couple of Jacobite Portrait Glasses which were probably produced in the nineteen-twenties, and the Royal Worcester vase of course.'

'How did the owners take it?' I asked.

'The one with the glasses isn't here at the moment so that was no problem, and the lady with the vase seemed more embarrassed than upset, so it's all been quite painless so far.'

'Good.'

My colleague drew a little closer. 'Have you seen the furniture stand yet? The one the organiser warned you about.'

'No. Why? Have you?'

76

'I think so. It's down there at the end. I see what she means,' he grinned.

'Is there anybody on it?' I asked.

'No, it's deserted.' He turned to continue his circuit of the hall, then turned back. 'Oh, I almost forgot. There's a bronze on the third stand from the end. I think it's a wrong'un, but you have a look at it.'

'Okay. If it looks wrong to me too, I'll just kick it out.'

'Fine.'

I made my way slowly down the hall, looking at each of the displays in turn until I reached quite a modest collection of ceramics, brass and copper. The long narrow table which fronted the stand was laid out with horse brasses, porcelain figures and bric-à-brac, none of which was particularly valuable. Standing in the middle of the table, however, was a bronze which I had no doubt was the one William had asked me to look at. It was a study of a horse standing with its neck outstretched as though it was sniffing the wind, while on the ground in front of it lay a pile of harness. It was large, almost certainly expensive, and looked strangely incongruous standing in the middle of all the other bits and bobs. As I stood looking at the piece I, in turn, was being closely observed by a couple seated behind the table. They were middle-aged and rather seedy, but I assumed they must be the proprietors of De Milo Antiques, who according to the slightly askew nameplate on the front of the table, were the exhibitors on that stand. Neither of them said a word or took their eyes off me for an instant as I reached for the small, white ticket which was looped around one of the bronze, equine legs. As expected, the neat, printed inscription gave the sculptor of the work as Pierre Jules Mene, and the asking price of £1,750.

Mene had been one of the leading nineteenth-century sculptors of animalier bronzes, and I could remember having seen two other examples of that particular cast

77

over the years. In each case the patination – the overall colour of the bronze – was green/brown, but this one was almost black, with a thick, oily texture that I didn't like at all.

The couple held me fixed in their mute gaze. She with her long, straight grey hair and sallow, sunken cheeks. He, overweight and balding with a sprinkling of dandruff over the shoulders of his brown cardigan. Neither spoke. They just sat and watched, sullen but alert. I took hold of the heavy bronze and lifted it from the table, turning it to look at the underside. Bright file marks scored the edges, and the steel nuts which held the horse in place on the base were covered with a superficial, brilliant orange rust, as though they had been deliberately dabbed with water within the last few days. No, I didn't like it at all. As far as I was concerned, William Baron was absolutely right: it was a copy. All I had to do now was break it to Mr and Mrs 'De Milo'.

I replaced the bronze very carefully among its surrounding bits and pieces and looked at the couple. Although the woman maintained her cold, suspicious gaze without even blinking, he suddenly looked away and cleared his throat. I began to suspect that what I was about to tell them wasn't going to come as a complete surprise.

'Good evening,' I said, 'I'm Richard Harton of Hampson's. I'm one of the team vetting the fair.'

'Hello,' the man said, looking at me sideways.

'And you are?' I asked, determined to extract their names from them if nothing else.

'Mr Plumley,' the man said, restricting to the absolute minimum the information being torn from him.

I looked at his companion and waited for an introduction. None came. I waited some more, then raised an eyebrow in what I hoped was a quizzical way, and went on waiting.

The leaden silence proved too much for Mr Plumley.

'And this is my wife – Mrs Plumley,' he said, grudgingly.

Mrs Plumley gave the most enigmatic of smiles then continued to stare at me.

'I'm afraid I'm not happy about this cast,' I said, addressing Mr Plumley, my hand on the bronze as I spoke.

'No?'

'No. There are several things about it I don't like, and putting them all together I just can't help but conclude that it's a recent copy.'

'Oh,' Mr Plumley said, without a hint of either surprise or emotion.

'So, I'm very sorry to say,' I went on, 'I have to ask you to withdraw it.'

'All right,' Mr Plumley agreed, placidly.

I looked at Mrs Plumley to see if she wanted to offer any resistance. But no, her passionless, blue-grey eyes just continued to stare out from below her lank grey fringe. Neither Plumley was going to put up any fight at all.

It was now quite clear to me that they had both known the horse to be bogus. They'd tried it on, failed, and now regarded it as a fair cop. I got the distinct impression that this was probably not the first fair the piece had been jettisoned from, and that it almost certainly wouldn't be the last. It was possible they were a pair of out and out rogues who specialised in this sort of thing, but I thought it more likely they'd simply strayed into an unfamiliar area, got their fingers seriously burnt, and were now trying to recoup their losses. Of course, none of that really mattered. The important thing was they shouldn't have been trying to pass the piece on as right, and they weren't going to get away with doing so at Dereford – thanks to the vigilance of the Hampson team!

Revelling rather in the absolute capitulation of the Plumleys, I decided to make a closer examination of one

79

other item which had caught my eye on the De Milo Antiques stand.

'The only other thing I'd like to have a quick look at is that fireback behind you,' I said.

Mr Plumley ran his fingers through the remains of his hair in what I felt was a gesture of frustration if not exasperation. A few new flecks of dandruff fluttered down like snowflakes onto his cardigan. Shrugging his shoulders in dumb capitulation he stepped aside and let me through.

The fireback was about two feet square and bore a coat of arms and the date '1672'. However, it was the back rather than the front that I was interested in. I eased the thing forward carefully. It was quite heavy enough to break a foot or even a leg if it fell, and it would certainly make a mess of what remained of the Plumley's stand if it crashed against one of their precious little display cabinets or tables.

I ran my hand along the back edge of the fireback and felt the grooves left by a coarse metal rasp. You couldn't see them for the thick application of lamp-black that now covered not only the fireback but me as well, but they were still there. I carefully leaned the piece against the wall again and stood up. The Plumleys still regarded me with the same baleful expressions.

'I'm afraid that will have to come out as well,' I said, 'it's quite new.'

'All right,' Mr Plumley agreed, once again without question.

I couldn't help but feel this was becoming rather unsatisfactory. As though the Plumleys, by their sheer bovine submissiveness, were making it impossible for me to give them their money's worth. I decided that whether they liked it or not I owed it to them to explain why I was rejecting their fireback.

'They make these,' I said, 'by taking an old fireback

and throwing it into wet sand to make a mould. Then they take it out and pour in the molten iron. Once it's cooled, hey presto, they've got a perfect copy of the original.'

Mr Plumley nodded. His wife simply continued to stare at me.

'The real giveaway,' I pressed on, despite the complete absence of audience participation, 'is that whoever filed off the rough raised lip that forms around the edge of the mould, did so as quickly as possible with a very coarse rasp. The marks of the rasp are still there, especially along the top edge. You'd never find marks like that on a three hundred year-old example,' I concluded, still hopeful of some reaction from Mr Plumley if not from his silent spouse.

'Oh,' he said, after a considerable pause.

I waited for a moment or two, then gave up. I knew when I was beaten.

'Well then,' I said, 'goodbye. I'm sorry to have spoilt your display.'

'Goodbye,' Mr Plumley said, as his wife, this time, gave an almost indiscernible nod.

An icy feeling ran down my spine as I stepped off the De Milo Antiques stand. I felt as though I had been in commune with the undead.

Despite the coded warnings I had received from both Julia Williams and William Baron, the Dereford Antiques stand still took me by surprise. It wasn't that it was full of fakes or anything like that. It was just that there didn't appear to be a single item on it that was pre-1860.

The stand groaned with late Victorian and Edwardian furniture, all unashamedly, accurately labelled and, for an antiques fair, not too outrageously priced, but it was *all* post-1860. I was so taken aback that I reversed the normal process and began scouring the stand for something I could approve, rather than the normal system of searching for the odd bit of reject. In the end, all my best efforts produced just one acceptable item. It was an early Victorian mahogany flush commode dating from about 1840, and its most notable feature was that, under its lid, it retained its original porcelain pan. I tried to picture in my mind's eye the stand, cleared of everything other than the commode. There it would be, spotlit, and raised up on a plinth – a sight to stir the soul of any right-minded Englishman. I decided I must be getting lightheaded and set off in search of Julia Williams.

I had no problem finding her. She was still on stage with Philip Lawrence absorbing what must have become the definitive lecture on Apostle Spoons.

' . . . yes, look at this one,' Philip was saying as I joined them. 'It's just the same as the others. The bowl's been reshaped to look like a seventeenth century spoon, the apostle figure's been slapped on the end of the handle, and the hall marks have been rubbed almost flat so you can't see what date it is. It's an out and out fake I'm afraid, just like the others. It began life as a straightforward George III tablespoon, and without any question it would be an offence to offer it for sale.'

'Yes, yes, I see now,' Julia Williams said, taking the spoon from the Hampson's silver specialist and looking at it even more closely. 'It's all so obvious when you explain it like that. I just can't think why I didn't spot they were forgeries before. I mean, they're just *so* obvious.'

'Oh, I don't know about that,' Philip countered, plainly not wishing his professional expertise to be underestimated or taken for granted in any way. 'You mustn't blame yourself. Before you can be confident about this sort of thing, it takes . . . well, it takes . . .'

'Years of experience and self-denial,' I offered.

He turned to me, his face wreathed in a particularly threatening smile. 'Something like that,' he said. 'Something like that.'

'Hello, Mr Harton,' Julia Williams said. 'Philip's been teaching me absolute masses about fake silver. I had no idea how little I knew. It's absolutely staggering, you know, on this stand alone there are nine fake Apostle Spoons, and he just spotted them straight away. He's *so* clever.'

'An absolute treasure,' I agreed as, unseen by his admiring pupil, Philip Lawrence mouthed something unpleasant at me.

'But how have *you* been getting on?' Mrs Williams continued. 'I'm afraid I haven't been very attentive.'

'Oh, no need to worry about that. I've been right through the place now and there are only a handful of pieces that I've rejected. A handful, that is, with the exception of the Dereford Antiques stand.'

'Oh, dear.'

'I take it that was the stand you were referring to when we arrived.'

'Yes, Mr Harton, it was. You do see the problem, obviously.'

'I do indeed. There's only one item on the entire stand that comes within the dateline.'

'Oh, dear,' she said, again. 'I was afraid this was going to happen.'

'But how could it happen? I asked. 'Didn't they know the fair was pre-1860 only?'

'It's a long story. As you might imagine, Dereford Antiques is based in the village, and over the years has carried some very good stock. Unfortunately, the man who runs it, Benny Carter, is in his seventies now, and just can't keep up with the sort of prices paid for eighteenth- and early nineteenth-century furniture.'

'So his stock's gone down-market?' I said.

'Exactly. I don't know much about furniture, but I think he still buys quality. It's just that it's all turn of the century or later.'

'Yes, the stuff on his stand is all good shipping material

83

as far as I could see.'

'That's it: every now and then you see a big container-lorry parked outside his shop, then for the next few weeks the place is empty.'

'But how is it he's exhibiting this stuff here?' I asked. 'I don't understand why he thought it would get past the vetting.'

'That's the problem,' Julia Williams replied, 'it's because he's always got away with it in the past.'

'What!' I was genuinely flabbergasted to think that Patrick Faulkner would have permitted such a flagrant breach of the dateline on a regular basis. 'You mean he gets away with this every year?'

'No, no, no,' Mrs Williams answered hurriedly. 'No – at least, not on this sort of scale.'

'On what sort of scale does he usually get away with then?'

'Oh, only the odd piece in the past,' she said, fidgeting uncomfortably. 'It's just suddenly mushroomed this year.'

I shrugged my shoulders in disbelief. 'Some mushroom!' I said.

'I know it all sounds impossibly corrupt and stupid,' she continued, 'but it really started out with people being kind. Benny's a real old character and very popular in the area, even if he is a bit cantankerous every now and then. Added to that, he was instrumental in starting and building up the Dereford Antiques Fair. I know it may not be particularly grand but it's developed quite a following over the years, and it was the first one to be held in the area.'

'Oh, I think it's first class,' Philip Lawrence interjected, 'and obviously extremely well run.'

'Oh, it's so kind of you to say so, Philip,' the organiser said, glowing a little. 'It really is an awful lot of hard work.'

'I'm sure it is,' he cooed.

84

I cleared my throat just to remind them I was still there. Julia Williams gave my colleague another grateful smile then continued. 'Yes, so, when the standard of Benny's stock started to fall nobody said anything. Anyway, he still used to buy good pieces every now and then, and hold them specifically for the fair. At worst there'd only be the odd item that should really have been rejected, and by common consent we hinted to the man who usually vetted the furniture . . . a big man . . . I can't remember his name . . .'

'Patrick Faulkner,' I suggested.

'That's right, Mr Faulkner – always tries to get me to have dinner with him afterwards . . . very persistent . . .'

This time it was Philip Lawrence who cleared his throat.

' . . . yes . . . anyway,' she picked up the threads of her story, 'he used to overlook the odd marginal piece, but this time it's just impossible.'

'I see,' I said. 'Has anybody spoken to Mr Carter about it?'

'I've tried, but he just won't listen. I even tried to get Mr Faulkner to give him a call, but when I telephoned him to suggest it, he explained he wasn't able to do the vetting this year and said it would be best if you handled it as the man on the spot.'

'I see,' I said again, suddenly getting a fresh perspective on Patrick Faulkner's prior engagement.

'There's no way round it, is there?' Julia Williams asked.

'Afraid not,' I said. 'You've either got to reject his stand or scrap your dateline.'

'We can't scrap the dateline,' she said, 'we've advertised it as usual, and it wouldn't be fair on the other exhibitors, would it?'

'No, it wouldn't. So that just leaves rejection of your Mr Carter's stand. Would you like me to scribble an explanatory note; I've got some Hampson's headed paper with me.'

'Oh, that would be a great help, Mr Harton,' she said, obviously relieved at the idea. 'I must say I'm not looking forward to telling him. It'll be much easier if it effectively comes from you.'

Chapter 7

Disingenuous though he might have been about his reasons for not vetting the Dereford Antiques Fair that particular year, Patrick Faulkner was certainly right about the other two points relating to the trip. Firstly, Julia Williams paid us one hundred and twenty pounds in used notes without a murmur, and secondly, The Plough and Furrow public house in Dereford was a fine place to settle down to supper on such an unpleasant night. Somehow, it had escaped the worst excesses of the wild-eyed young men in the big brewery marketing departments who spend their waking hours ripping out genuine old pub interiors so that they can then get paid for replacing them with fake old pub interiors. Nobody had ever tried to knock the Plough and Furrow's three bars into one, fit electric pumps on the beer taps so they would always measure precisely half a pint, or pipe the musical equivalent of red flock wallpaper into the bars through loudly buzzing speakers.

It was a proper pub. In the saloon bar an aromatic log fire crackled away cheerfully on the stone hearth, giving the low-ceilinged room a cosy glow. The combination of the flickering flames, the old black oak beams and the mellow red brick floor had an immediate soothing effect on us all.

'This is more like it,' Philip Lawrence said.

'Yes,' William added, as he went over and stood with his back to the blazing fire, 'there is a God after all.'

87

'I do believe you're beginning to get over losing the toss back there in the hall, William,' I said.

'Oh, I don't mind,' he replied. 'After all, somebody has to stay sober and drive, and it does carry the added bonus of meaning I won't have to sit in the back this time.'

As Philip got the drinks at the hole in the wall that served as a bar, I looked around the room. It was furnished entirely with nineteenth-century country pieces: two oak settles, several oak tripod tables and lots of Victorian Windsor chairs and smoker's chairs. All good old pub furniture which, by that time, you were far more likely to come across in an auction room than a hostelry. It was a real little Aladdin's cave.

'Come on, Richard,' Philip interrupted my musing, 'stop salivating over the furnishings and pay attention to the menu. According to the landlady, all they can manage for us is home-made vegetable soup, home-made steak and kidney pie, home-cured ham, egg and chips, farmhouse Cheddar, Stilton that will melt on your tongue, and home-baked granary rolls.'

'What! No sliced white bread or frozen gristle-burgers?' I asked.

'Fresh out apparently,' he confirmed.

'Well, I think it's a disgrace,' William said, settling into the seat closest to the fire. 'This is the sort of thing that's ruining the reputation of British catering. I suggest we find the nearest motorway service station immediately.'

An hour and a quarter later we were seated by the inglenook, contemplating our drinks and what little remained of an excellent meal. There had been three couples eating in the bar when we arrived, but they had now gone, leaving us the only beneficiaries of the saloon ambience. But if trade was slow in our bar, it was being compensated for elsewhere in the pub. A low, rolling, background babble of conversation punctuated by regular outbursts of noisy laughter had grown in

88

volume in the next-door bar as the evening had gone on.

'Sounds as though it's all go in the public bar tonight,' remarked Philip.

'Yes,' I said. 'The only thing that surprises me is that it's not jumping in here as well.'

'Oh, you know what a tight bunch saloon bar drinkers are,' he said. 'I expect they'll arrive ten minutes before last orders and . . .'

He was interrupted by the noisy rattling of the old door latch. All three of us turned to see who was about to violate our privacy.

It turned out to be an elderly, sharp featured, wiry little man with a pronounced stoop. Seeming not to notice us, he took off his coat, tossed it onto one of the chairs just inside the door, and then hobbled over to the counter.

For no reason at all, we three sat watching him in silence as the landlady appeared in the hatchway.

'Hello, darling. You're late tonight. Pint of the usual?' she said, reaching up to the shelf above her for a glass.

'No, Doris, no, you'd better give me a whisky, girl.'

'Whisky?' she said, obviously surprised at what was a departure from the old boy's normal drinking habits. 'What sort, my dear?'

'Black Label, and make it a large one, Doris.'

'Goodness, sweetheart, you must be celebrating something.'

'Cor!' he snorted, angrily, 'I should think I am. I should think I am.'

'Why, what's the matter, love? What's . . .'

The landlady was stopped by a noisy demand for service in the public bar. She patted the old man's hand, assured him she would be back in a minute and turned away to deal with her more pressing clientele.

I continued to watch the old chap as he picked up a jug from the counter and added a splash of water to his glass. His hands, bony and twisted with age, trembled a little, so that the jug clinked noisily against the glass. He took a shaky but sizeable swig of whisky, and momentarily drew himself upright as the spirit sent a responsive shiver through him. Returning to his original bent stance, he turned for the first time and looked across the room to the fire where we sat.

An expression of surprise mingled with satisfaction swept over his features.

'Evening,' he said, immediately starting to cross the bar towards us.

'Good evening,' I replied.

'Time we were going, boys,' Philip hissed out of the side of his mouth. 'Here comes a "This Was My Life" character if ever I've seen one.'

I didn't doubt it. There was a sense of purpose about the way the old boy was swooping down on us: like an eagle on a lamb. He was clearly the resident pub bore – lonely, fed-up, and only too willing to tell anyone who stood still long enough, why.

'Dirty old night,' he said, positioning himself with his back to the fire and putting his drink down on our table in a clear declaration that he was now a member of our party.

'Yes,' I said, 'not nice at all.'

'Come far?' he asked, as he massaged his lower back with his claw-like fingers.

'On our way to London,' William said.

He nodded. 'What d'you do, then?'

Being able to admit to being a fine art auctioneer does have its advantages. Used responsibly, the disclosure can impress and intrigue – 'Gosh, how *interesting* . . . I bet *it's* really interesting . . . I bet *you're* really interesting . . . Yes, I'd *love* to have dinner with you . . . ' etc, etc. However, careless use can result in long hours of torture – 'Mummy, this is Richard, he's an auctioneer . . . no I'm sure he'd love to spend the evening looking at all your dirty old china and giving you a free valuation on everything . . .!'

No, there are definitely times when it's nothing short of foolhardy for an auctioneer to own up to his profession. Much wiser to choose something safe and boring that nobody's interested in. It was obvious to us all that that evening in the Plough and Furrow at Dereford was just such an occasion.

'We're accountants,' I said.

' . . . solicitors,' replied Philip, at precisely the same moment.

William Baron, less experienced in the gentle art of subterfuge than we were, was slower off the mark, and was consequently left open-mouthed and silent. This turned out to be fortunate since he confided later he had favoured 'merchant bankers' as his reply.

The old man looked confused.

'He's a solicitor,' I said hastily, pointing to Philip, 'and my colleague, here, and I are chartered accountants.'

My clarification of our respective roles seemed to more than satisfy our companion.

'What brings you to Dereford, then?' he asked, rubbing his hands behind his back.

'We specialise in mergers and acquisitions,' Philip said, with enough authority to almost convince me, let alone the old man, 'and we've been visiting a client.'

'Someone in Oxford, I suppose.'

'I'm afraid it's absolutely confidential,' William chipped in, joining in the spirit of things. 'It would play hell with the share values if news of negotiations leaked out.'

'Oh, yes, of course – I know what you mean,' the old man said, dropping his voice and slyly tapping the side of his nose with his finger. 'Mind you, I could do with a nice hot tip like that after the day I've had.'

'Why? What's happened . . . ' William winced and clutched at his shin under the table as both Philip's kick and my own found their target.

'Well, it makes me want to spit just thinking about it . . .'

'Yes, well, there it is then . . . ' Philip strted to rise from his chair as he spoke.

' . . . but you tell me if you think it's fair,' the old man continued, pulling up a chair and effectively boxing us in.

'We'd love to,' I said, 'but, unfortunately we really must make tracks for London – early start tomorrow and all that . . .'

'Oh, it won't take a minute,' he said, 'and I'll get some more drinks when Doris gets back – if she ever does,' he added, glancing in the direction of the hatch.

'I'm afraid . . . ' I persisted.

'I'm an antique dealer, see?' he pressed on. 'I've been in the trade for sixty years, man and boy. Then today some wet-behind-the-ears, toffee-nosed know-nothing from London, who's barely into long trousers, has just come over here and kicked all my furniture out of my own antiques fair. Eh! What d'you make of that then? Eh?'

'It sounds absolutely appalling,' Philip said, settling back into his chair, his face suddenly a picture of deep concern. 'How could such a thing be allowed to happen?'

'You may well ask. You may well ask,' the old man replied, taking out a large spotted handkerchief and swiping at the dewdrop which had gathered on the tip of his nose. He gave a long, loud blow, another wipe, thrust the handkerchief back into his pocket, and continued: 'I was the first dealer in this area. I was the one who started the Dereford Antiques Fair. I've had more fine furniture through my hands than that jumped-up little sod's had hot dinners. But none of that counts for nothing – not nowadays it doesn't. Nothing, that's what it's worth.' He stared morosely at the empty glass in his hand.

'Let me get you another,' Philip said, standing up and taking the man's glass. 'After a dreadful experience like that, I think you deserve it.'

I glared at my colleague as he reached out for my glass. It was a look he repaid with a particularly innocent smile.

'Another half?' he said.

'I really do think we should be going,' I insisted.

'No, no, bags of time,' he replied, ambling over to the bar, 'bags of time.'

I reconciled myself to what was to come. Sitting through the old man's venomous attacks, incognito, promised to be as much fun as reading one's own obituary after all the good bits have been edited out.

'So what did this character claim was wrong with your furniture?' Philip asked when he returned to the table. It was the verbal equivalent of lighting the old man's blue touchpaper.

'Sod all!' he spat. 'Absolutely sod all. And how could he claim there was anything wrong with it? It was all good stuff.'

'But, surely he must have given some reason for rejecting it,' I said, recalling the diplomatically worded letter I had left with Julia Williams.

'None! No reason at all!' the old man replied, intercepting another dewdrop at the precise moment it detached itself from the tip of his nose.

'But didn't he . . . ' I hesitated. I was supposed to be an accountant. I didn't want to appear to know too much about this business. 'Didn't he . . .'

'Leave a note or anything?' Philip cut in, brightly.

'A note? Oh, yes, he left me a note all right. Gave it to that Williams woman before he high-tailed it back to his plush London office, in his flash company car.'

In response to hearing Hampson's valuations office and my departmental Mini being described respectively as 'plush' and 'flash', William had the decency to choke on his orange juice.

'I say, be careful,' Philip said, leaning across and dealing him a series of terrifying thumps on the back. 'We don't want you expiring. You're the driver.'

'But what did it say?' I persisted.

'What?' the old man said vaguely, as he turned his attention from the gurgling William back to me.

'The note – what did it say about why your furniture was rejected?'

'Oh, that.' He took another swig from his glass and smacked his lips. 'I don't know.'

'You don't know?' I said, fighting back the impulse to grab him by the throat and shake him till his head fell off.

'No, I don't know.'

'But . . . didn't you . . . haven't you . . . read it?' I asked, with all the nonchalance I could muster.

'Read it? Read it?' the old man snorted, as spirit-assisted colour flushed his cheeks. 'Why should I have read it? What could that young whipper-snapper tell me about furniture? It would have been a different matter if it had been Faulkner – he knows a bit, he does. But, he would never have chucked my stuff out anyway. He knows quality when he sees it, he does.' He took another sip from his glass. 'No, I'm not going to start reading lectures from schoolboys at my age.'

'May I ask how old you are?' William said.

'Guess.'

'Oh, seventy . . . seventy-one . . .?'

'I'm eighty-two,' he declared, with obvious satisfaction.

'That's remarkable,' William commented. 'Do let me buy you a drink.'

'Well, that's very kind of you, young man. I don't suppose one more whisky will do me any harm.'

'I don't suppose it will,' William said. 'What about you two?'

Philip made room for another half but I shook my head.

As William made his way to the bar, I had one last try.

'But, surely he would have explained in the letter why he'd rejected your things.'

'What?' the old man asked, more intent on William's generosity than my logic.

'The letter . . .'

The old door latch rattled once more, heralding the arrival of another customer.

'Marty!' the old boy shouted, gleefully. 'What are you having, son?'

The customer was a big man. In fact, he was a very big man. He was probably in his late forties but he had the physique of a weightlifter. He was dark, with wavy hair greying at the temples. His overcoat looked to be mohair, while his shoes were patent leather. There was no doubt: he was a dealer.

'Hello, Benny. How are you? Still getting younger I see.'

Glowing at the compliment, the old man rose a little unsteadily to his feet. 'What're you having, Marty?' he asked once more.

'No, no, maestro. I'll get 'em. What's it to be?'

'Well, as it happens, this young gent's just getting me one,' our elderly friend explained, pointing to William at the counter.

The young gent forced a smile, cleared his throat and addressed the newcomer: 'Perhaps I could get you one as well?'

'That'd be very nice. I'll have a brandy, thanks.'

William Baron's smile trembled on his lips as he tried to make his facial muscles advertise an emotion some way removed from the one he was actually feeling. 'A brandy,' he confirmed, 'of course.'

'He's an accountant,' the old man added, as though it needed explanation.

'Is he, by God!' boomed the man in the mohair. 'You'd better make it a double, then. Cos if *you* can't fiddle it on expenses, nobody can.' His laugh was deep

95

and resonant, and was quickly complimented by the falsetto cackle of our companion.

William's smile trembled once more and vanished.

As the enlarged party regrouped around the fire, the old man introduced his associate: 'This is Marty Cohen – I've known him since he was in short trousers, and his dad before him.'

The vast Mr Cohen nodded to the assembled company.

'Did you here what that bastard from Hampson's did to me today?' the old man continued, turning to Cohen.

'Yes, Benny, I heard. But you're not the only one mate. A few others got done over as well – not that that's any consolation to you, of course.'

'Who else did he knobble?' the old man asked, with the sort of eagerness the elderly often reserve for obtaining details of the demise of a contemporary friend.

'Well, there was poor old Ma Plumley, and you know what a dreadful state she's in.'

'Yes, cancer again, isn't it?'

'Yeah, poor old girl. One-way ticket this time, I think.'

'Bloody shame,' the old man said, then brightening up: 'What did he sling out there?'

'That big Mene bronze they've been carting around for the past eighteen months.'

'Yes? Bloody shame. Mind you, it was about as right as a nine bob note,' the old fellow cackled maliciously as he spoke.

'Oh, yeah,' his companion agreed, 'they ain't complaining. It was a wrong'un. They could have just done without the hassle. They had a fireback kicked out as well by the same bloke, but they ain't complaining.'

'Well, I bloody well am,' Benny Carter grumbled, staggering to his feet again, 'and so's my bladder. I must go and splash me boots – I'll be back in a minute.'

We all observed the old man in silence as he made his way to the door. It wasn't as direct a route as it might

96

have been, but it was unassisted, and after what he'd consumed that was an achievement in itself.

'He's a character,' Marty Cohen commented, once the old boy was safely out of the bar. 'Marvellous really.'

'Yes,' Philip agreed. 'Shame about this business of his stand being rejected at the local antiques fair, though.'

I didn't care. Philip could do his worst. I simply determined that I wouldn't say another word on the subject.

'Oh, he's been telling you all about it, has he? Hard luck. Between you and me, it was entirely his own fault. Well, his and the organiser's. There's been a dateline of 1860 on that fair for ages, and old Benny's been getting away with a tiny bit here and a tiny bit there for several years now. It should have been stamped on at the beginning but that daft bird who runs the show couldn't bring herself to do it. Hampson's would chuck a couple of bits off Benny's stand, and he'd have 'em back on again as soon as the bloke had got out of the door. It was ridiculous.'

'So, the chap who vetted it wasn't at fault, then?' I asked, abandoning my resolution not to say any more on the subject.

'No, he's done us all a favour. I know old Benny never pretended any of his stuff was right, but it's still bloody silly to have a stand full of Edwardian furniture smack in the middle of a fair with an 1860 dateline. No, I'd buy the Hampson's bloke a bloody good drink if he walked in here now – as long as Benny was still in the gents, that is.'

The rattling door latch proclaimed the return of the man himself. Having carefully closed the door, he launched out across the room towards us. Although his unsteadiness hadn't improved, it didn't seem to have got any worse either, so he reached the safe haven of his chair without too much trouble.

'So,' he said to Marty Cohen, 'you didn't have any trouble with this little twit from Hampson's then?'

'Not with him, no. But he brought a friend with him, and if I ever get my hands on him, I'll unscrew his head.' Cohen cracked his fingers one by one, ominously, as he spoke.

'Why?' Benny Carter asked, once again giving the high-pitched cackle that I, for one, was beginning to find exceedingly irritating. 'What'd he chuck out, Marty?'

'Every one of my bloody Apostle Spoons.'

'No!'

'Every bloody one.'

'Cor, I'll be damned!'

Philip Lawrence was suddenly very quiet. Until then he'd been on top, bubbly form. The whole situation might have been tailor-made to fit his anarchic sense of humour. All he'd had to do was give a little tweak here, a little tweak there, and the whole thing had rolled along nicely. All at once, however, it appeared that he'd lost his appetite and enthusiasm for it. He wasn't finding the joke funny any more, and he didn't seem as relaxed as he had been earlier. He fidgeted in his chair next to the mountainous figure of Marty Cohen, looking at his watch repeatedly and gulping down his drink far too quickly for his own good. As Cohen went into some depth about the disappointment he felt over his rejected spoons, and then into considerable detail about what he'd like to do to Hampson's silver expert, I noticed that my friend was displaying some signs of serious agitation. This was strange, because, for the first time all evening since the arrival of Mr Carter, I was really beginning to enjoy myself.

'. . . and as far as I'm concerned,' Marty Cohen growled, 'the whole bloody lot can go up to Goldsmiths Hall, and the Plate Committee can decide whether they're wrong or not.'

'That's right, son,' Benny Carter agreed, as an untended dewdrop cascaded to the floor, 'you take the bastards on.'

'I've got a good mind to,' Cohen confirmed. 'At least, I would if I had the time.'

'That's the problem,' the old man commiserated, as he drained his glass, 'it's all right for the likes of the chinless wonders at Hampson's. They get paid whether they do anything or not. But the likes of you and me go under if we don't make a turn each day.'

'Yeah,' Marty Cohen agreed, emptying his own glass, 'I'll end up unloading the bloody things somewhere else I expect, just to save the time. Mind you, one day I'm going to walk into Hampson's silver department and catch the sod by the throat.'

'I should,' I said.

Cohen put his empty glass on the table and turned to Benny Carter. 'Come on, maestro, I'll give you a lift home.'

The old man was winched from his chair and assisted to the door by his friend. As he steered Carter out into the night, Marty Cohen turned to bid us goodnight. '. . . and you stay with accountancy, gents,' he concluded. 'There's nothing but grief in this bloody business.'

'Comfortable in the back there?' I asked.

'No,' came the sullen reply.

'Never mind,' William commented, 'not far to go now. Anyway, you've slept through most of the journey.'

'Sleep! Sleep!' Philip complained. 'That wasn't sleep. That was a series of very nasty nightmares, and they all featured Mr Marty Cohen.'

'There, there,' I said, 'it was only a dream. It's all over now.'

'It certainly will be if he ever turns up in the silver department,' William added. 'Did you see the size of his shoulders? He looked like an American footballer in full kit.'

'Thank you, you're making me feel much better,' Philip said.

'I don't know what you're making so much fuss about,' I said. 'You didn't seem very concerned when you were busy baiting Benny Carter.'

'May I remind you,' said the voice in the back of the car, 'that Benny Carter was eighty-two, weighed in at no more than eight stone, and could be knocked over by a stiff breeze. Marty Cohen, however, looked a very fit forty-five, was constructed entirely of muscle, and could obviously kill with his bare eyelids.'

'Would you like flowers or charitable donations?' I asked.

'Cash only, and I want it now – I intend to flee to South America.'

'If we could be serious for a moment,' William said.

'So, who's not being serious?' came the reply from behind us.

'*If* we can be serious?' William repeated. 'What did he mean about taking the spoons to Goldsmiths Hall?'

'It was an idle threat,' Philip replied.

'If you say so, but what did he mean?'

'The Plate Committee of the Worshipful Company of Goldsmiths and Silversmiths is the last word on whether a piece of silver is right or wrong,' Philip explained. 'It's an offence to add to a piece of silver that's already been hallmarked unless it's then re-assayed, and it's an offence to offer a piece of silver like that for sale anywhere in the UK unless it's been re-assayed.'

'So, if the Plate Committee agreed with you that the spoons were wrong, he couldn't sell them unless they were hallmarked with this year's date letter?'

'Yes, and what do you mean "if" the Plate Committee agreed with me . . .?'

'Treat him with care, William,' I advised. 'He seems to be a bit sensitive all of a sudden.'

'So, what do you think he'll do with them?' William continued.

'He'll unload them quietly somewhere,' said the

100

disembodied voice behind us. 'He certainly won't risk a hundred per cent loss by taking them to the Plate Committee.'

'No,' I said, 'much easier just to come round to Hampson's and unscrew your head.'

'Richard . . .'

'Yes, Philip.'

'Shut-up . . .'

'Yes, Philip.'

Chapter 8

The daily post bag did not seem to be improving. There was always the possibility that juicy instructions were waiting to be sorted in the mail next door but, if what had been sitting on the doormat of the valuations office was anything to go by, there was little doubt I was best advised not to hold my breath.

With the exception of a small cheque in settlement of a long overdue account for a valuation carried out before my time, the entire morning's post was committed to the wastepaper basket. I noted with some satisfaction that the amount of practice I was getting at this basic filing technique was at least resulting in vastly improved accuracy on my part. Despite having moved the waste bin a yard further away from where I sat, the three circulars dropped straight in, and the invitation to take out accident insurance – 'You never know when tragedy might strike!' – bounced in off the rim. Only the details of a mail order catalogue failed to find their target, and four out of five wasn't bad.

Next, I turned to contemplating the thick, muddy liquid in my mug and wondered why instant coffee always tasted like *instant* coffee rather than coffee. Then I wondered why people drank it. After all, if it was the taste of coffee they wanted, they weren't getting it. Then I wondered why *I* was drinking it. The only reason I could think of was convenience. It then struck me that convenience in itself was clearly not good enough reason for drinking something I didn't like, and which was probably bad for me anyway. I resolved to stop drinking instant coffee forthwith. At least my early start to the day had resulted in one decision.

I heard the street door open then close again, then Charlotte's footsteps on the stairs. A few moments later she waddled into the office, almost completely hidden beneath an arrangement of woolly hat, coat and long trailing scarf. Peeping out from between the protective layers her eyes watered with the cold, and her nose shone like a bright red beacon.

'God, it's freezing,' she mumbled, throwing her gloves onto her desk and warming her hands on the radiator.

'You cycled in, I take it,' I observed.

'Yes, the bus takes an age at the moment.'

She hung up her things and sat down at her desk. Opening her bag, she took out her glasses and put them on so they were perched on the end of her nose. Next, she sharpened a pencil, picked up a notebook and sat there, looking at me.

'And my tasks for today are?' she said.

'Number one – beg, borrow or steal a coffee percolator from somewhere.'

'Check.'

'Number two – obtain a supply of real coffee – by the same means if possible.'

'Right.'

'Number three – make coffee.'

'Well, that should take care of the morning. What would you like me to do this afternoon?'

'I don't know. I haven't got a number four yet.'

She put down the notebook and pencil, and pushed her glasses back into place. 'No great rush of business yet, then?'

'No. And never mind about a rush. I'd be content with a trickle just at the moment.'

'It's bound to be slow at this time of the year, Richard.

I'm sure things will start to pick up soon.'

'They need to. I hadn't expected it to be this dead.'

'I'm sure it will get . . .'

Charlotte was interrupted by the unfamiliar sound of her telephone ringing.

'Steady! Don't panic!' I said, 'but it could be a client.'

'I can handle it. Trust me,' she replied, picking up the phone. 'Valuations office – Good morn . . . yes, he is . . . hold on, Mr Derby, I'll put you through.'

I reached out, ready to pick up my telephone as soon as she transferred the call.

'Sounds a bit grumpy to me,' she whispered.

'Morning, Richard. Has anybody spoken to you about the Bailey's sale this morning?'

'Good morning, Bob. No, not a word – what sale?'

'Their first one since the Christmas break. You should have been told all about it. Sometimes I think I'm the only one in this building who does any work . . .'

'Okay, I'll . . .'

'You'll have to get yourself down there – they're in Twickenham. I want you to take their sales on a regular basis now, anyway. Hampson's has provided them with auctioneers as a favour ever since Don Bailey, the owner, had his stroke. It's in our interests – they take all our junk so I don't want them to fold. There's only two hundred lots today. The sale starts at eleven so you'll be finished by one at the latest. Speak to Harry Sutton when you get there – he pretty well runs the place these days.'

'All right. What about balancing the books after the sale and so on?'

'Don't for God's sake get involved in any of that. All you have to do is take the sale.'

'Right.'

'Now, I've given some thought to promoting your department.'

'Yes.'

'As you know, I'm not convinced about the advertising you want.'

'Well, I do think we . . .'

'So, we'll concentrate on the probate work and get some lunches organised. My girl can set them up, so let her know of anybody you'd particularly like to see on the guest list – okay?'

'Yes, fine . . .'

'And explain to Miss Morrison that I am not *grumpy*, just *busy* – there is a difference.'

Before I could reply, he'd put his telephone down.

'What was all that about?' Charlotte asked.

'I've got to take the Bailey's auction this morning . . .'

'Oh, you poor thing,' she said, crossing herself, 'you'll probably come back with bubonic plague or something. That place is a tip. It should be condemned as a health hazard.'

' . . . and he's not prepared to advertise the insurance side of our business, although he is going to put on lunches for solicitors . . .'

'I'll brace myself for the rush of work.'

' . . . and he's the only one who works in this company . . .'

'Oh, knickers to him!'

' . . . and he specifically asked me to explain to you that he's not *grumpy*, just *busy*, and that there is a difference.'

'Aaah! He heard me?'

'Afraid so.'

Charlotte leant forward and drummed the desk with her clenched fists. 'I hate him! I hate him! How does he always do that to me? He must have X-ray ears or something.'

'I don't think X-ray ears would give him much of an advantage,' I said. 'It would be about as much use as having stereophonic eyes.'

'Oh, shut up! You know what I mean.'

Charlotte was still fuming gently when, almost without precedent, the phone rang for the second time in under ten minutes.

'It's a Mr Parkinson for you,' she said, 'about a valuation he needs urgently.'

'Put him on.'

Mr Parkinson explained that he was a partner in the West End solicitors, Hallworth, Jolly and Phillimore. He went on to say he'd never used Hampson's before, and the only reason he was contemplating doing so now was because none of the other auctioneers in London (and he had spoken to them all) could do the job in time. Clearly, Mr Parkinson did not believe in sugar-coating pills.

'When does it have to be done?' I asked.

'This afternoon.'

'Are any items likely to be sold?'

'Not in the foreseeable future. We have instructions to put everything in store – though Lord knows why!'

It seemed that all we were likely to get out of this job was the valuation fee: not much of a carrot at such short notice.

'What sort of items are we talking about?' I asked.

'Mainly furniture, in poor condition. There's not much of it. It's only a one-bedroomed flat in Chichester Court, Belgravia. Can you do it?'

'Yes, I can be there at three.'

'Good. I'll meet you in the foyer.'

I jotted down the details in my diary as I replaced the receiver.

'What did it sound like?' Charlotte asked.

'Not very exciting, but it's work, and doing this one for them at such short notice might just encourage Messrs Hallworth, Jolly and Phillimore to push something else our way. We can but hope.'

No more than five minutes later the telephone gave voice again.

'I don't believe it,' I said. 'If it goes on like this we'll have to employ more staff.'

'I know,' Charlotte replied, 'I'm not sure I can stand the pressure . . . hello, Valuations Office . . . yes . . . yes . . . yes, we do . . . fine, if you could just hold on a moment, I'll transfer you to Mr Harton, the manager, who I'm sure will be able to advise you . . . and what was the name, madam . . .?'

Edwina Randolph-Bruce sounded rather elderly but very nice. What was more, she knew what she wanted. It was an insurance valuation of the contents of her flat near Marble Arch. She'd never had one done before, she'd got no silver or jewellery to speak of, but she did have a lot of oriental porcelain collected by her late husband. She didn't ask what it would cost, just when I could do it. She appeared to be an ideal client.

'Great!' Charlotte said. 'Did she say why she'd chosen Hampson's?'

'Yes, and it does nothing for my argument for an advertising budget; she came to us because she and her husband bought a picture here twenty-five years ago, and she remembered that the auctioneer was "terribly polite".'

'Oh, I see what you mean.'

'Mind you, I suppose we could build a campaign around it – "Hampson's, the terribly polite auctioneers" . . .'

Yet again the telephone jangled on Charlotte's desk. This time there was no doubt about it: this much activitiy constituted a boom. Never before had we received four telephone calls prior to half-past nine in the morning. Sometimes we hadn't received that many by half-past nine at night. It was definitely a record.

Just for a change, I took this one on my line. 'Good morning, Hampson's Valuations Office.'

'Hello, Mr Harton.' It was a woman's voice – a soft, American accent. 'I suppose you've already got a flat by now, haven't you?'

'Lady Barnes?'

'Yes, it's Dorothy Barnes. I thought I'd just call and let you know that the girl I offered the flat to turned out to be not all she pretended. In fact, she turned out to be almost nothing she pretended.'

'I'm sorry,' I said. 'But, does that mean the flat's available again?'

'Oh, yes, it's available, but I don't suppose you want it any more . . . do you?'

Charlotte and I sat looking at one another, neither of us speaking for fear of breaking the spell that seemed to have fallen on the office. In the space of forty-five minutes we had booked in two valuations and I'd got a place to live. Not just any place, either. It was the flat I had set my heart on and then been forced to forget. Now, suddenly, it was mine. It was hard not to feel that the tide had turned. It was flowing in my favour.

'I must head down to Bailey's in a moment,' I said, 'but I'll just pop next door and see if William Baron can come with me to have a look at the porcelain on that insurance valuation.'

'You might be able to persuade his boss to go instead.'

'What, Bernard Thornton? I've not even met him yet.'

'Well, now's your chance. He's back. I saw him walking up the street this morning when I arrived.'

When I had asked Philip Lawrence what he thought of Bernard Thornton he'd been uncharacteristically vague. Not that he had hesitated regarding his professional ability, that wasn't in question. It was the man himself that he seemed unsure of.

'I don't know,' he'd concluded, 'you'll have to make up your own mind. I'm not sure whether he's genuinely an eccentric or whether he just puts it on for effect. He was educated at Winchester, and that could explain a lot – every Wykehamist I've ever met has been slightly dotty.'

Charlotte had agreed with Philip's assessment and had

108

also been reluctant to come down one way or the other on the eccentricity issue. It seemed that I would have to make my own assessment of the Director of Hampson's Ceramics Department.

A single customer was standing at the first floor reception desk when I reached the top of the stairs. An unprepossessing little man in a cheap raincoat and plastic shoes, he was very carefully unpacking things from a carrier bag which stood on the floor beside him. Each piece was wrapped in newspaper, and as the assortment of items on the counter grew, so did the mountain of discarded newsprint. He chattered away nervously as he continued to pull parcel after parcel from the bulging bag: 'Oh, now, this is the . . . er . . . no it's not . . . it's the . . . er . . . oh, no it isn't . . . ah, it's . . . it's the other one after all . . .!'

All of this was going on under the bored gaze of a member of Hampson's staff whom I instantly recognised as my quarry – Bernard Thornton.

His appearance, if not distinguished in the accepted sense of the word, was certainly singular. Although he stood bent forward, with his elbows resting on the counter, the impression he gave was that of a very big man. There was an ursine quality about him which was exaggerated by the thatch of greying, dark hair which hung down over his forehead. He wore a badly knotted shocking pink bow tie which clashed with his red striped shirt, and a tweed jacket with leather elbow patches. The overall impression was that of a donnish public schoolmaster who, plucked from his books against his will and dropped into the metropolis, was either unaware of the conventions of dress in his new surroundings or just didn't give a damn for them anyway.

As I studied him, he continued to lean on the counter, head down, hands clasped before him. The only sign of movement was in his thumbs: he was

109

twiddling them at high speed, first one way then the other, faster and faster until, abruptly, they stopped.

'Remarkable!' he boomed, snatching up the latest item to have appeared from the tabloid pages. 'Absolutely remarkable!'

The surprised figure in the raincoat flinched and stepped backwards in response to Bernard Thornton's unheralded, almost volcanic, eruption. And I could understand his concern. As the previously dormant ceramics specialist lurched over to the window to hold the piece up to the light, he was a discordant symphony of flailing legs and windmilling arms.

I strained to see what was responsible for the outburst, but as far as I could tell from where I was standing it was no more than a small, garishly coloured glass vase.

'As I thought,' Thornton said, placing the piece back on the counter, 'just as I thought.' He gave the petrified little man a big smile, rubbed his hands together as furiously as he had earlier twiddled his thumbs, then he bent forward over the piece so that he was nose to nose with its shrinking owner. 'Don't move a muscle,' he instructed, 'just wait here. I want my assistant to see this.'

He turned to go, stopped, turned back and gave the man another huge grin. 'You don't mind, do you?' he asked. 'Only it's not every day he'll get the opportunity to see a piece of this quality?'

Struck dumb, the man shook his head vigorously.

'So kind,' Thornton said, still beaming, 'so very kind.' He went to the door that led to the Ceramics Department, opened it and called out: 'Oh, William! Come out here! There's a piece you really must see.' He then ambled back to the desk and stood there, arms folded across his barrel chest, looking down at the vase with an expression of almost mystical awe.

Despite wanting to have a closer look at the thing, I

continued to hover near the top of the stairs. If I approached the reception desk I would have to introduce myself to Bernard Thornton, and in his present, enthusiastic mood he might just seek my opinion on the vase. That would create a problem since I didn't have an opinion on the vase. Or more correctly, the opinion I held on the vase seemed far removed from that held by Bernard Thornton. All in all it did not seem an appropriate moment to expose my complete ignorance of an item which Thornton obviously rated very highly, but which I would have consigned to the dustbin. So, I continued to loiter in the shadows.

We all waited in silence for a few moments, then the door to the Ceramics Department opened again and William Baron, still in the act of putting on his jacket, appeared on the scene.

Without acknowledging my presence he went straight to the counter where his boss stood motionless, looking down at the brightly coloured vase.

'Ah, William!' Bernard Thornton exploded into life, once again making the little man flinch. 'Look! Look at this. Gaze on it. Tell me what you see. Speak to me as it speaks to you, William. What does this remarkable little piece say to you? What is it saying?' As he spoke, Thornton held the vase up between finger and thumb and rotated it before his assistant's eyes.

'Well ... er ... to me it says ... ' William Baron hesitated, 'to me it says ... absolutely nothing, I'm afraid, Bernard. Have I gone deaf?'

'Yes!' Thornton barked, causing the little man in the raincoat to leap back another pace as though he had received an electric shock. 'This, William, is a remarkable piece, and I will tell you why. Look, listen and learn!'

111

Chapter 9

Bernard Thornton replaced the glass vase on the counter, leant forward on his elbows and clasped his hands together.

'This piece of glass,' he said, in a hoarse, stage-whisper, 'is indeed remarkable.'

The courage which had so recently deserted the raincoated owner now returned. Boosted by the imminence of an announcement of a windfall, and by Thornton's sudden, calm intimacy, he drew close to the counter again and bent forward to look at his treasure. Even William Baron stooped down to get a better view. I edged closer to the huddled figures so as not to miss anything.

'It is, of course . . . ' Thornton paused to give his words maximum dramatic effect, ' . . . absolutely . . . *worthless.*'

For a moment, the little man didn't seem to take in what had been said. He just continued staring expectantly at the vase while nervously licking his lips, his tongue darting in and out like a lizard's. Then the full moment of Bernard Thornton's verdict hit him, and his shoulders sagged as if a heavy burden had been laid across them. Open-mouthed and clearly confused he looked up at the once again beaming countenance of the ceramics specialist.

'Er . . . ' the man cleared his throat, ' . . . er . . . worthless?'

'Oh, yes, absolutely.'

'But ... but, you said it was remarkable ... you said . . .'

'Yes, and it is indeed remarkable. But not because it's a rare and wonderful work of art. I mean, just look at it,' Bernard Thornton held the vase aloft once more, 'it's absolutely awful. It's Woolworth's at its worst. It's Christmas cracker material. It's almost obscene in its ugliness. No, no, the remarkable thing about this dreadful little vase is that you brought it in to us.'

The dejected owner looked completely nonplussed.

'You looked at this vase,' Thornton continued, enthusiastically throwing his arms about as though he were trying to get rid of them, 'and you thought: "I must get Hampson's to look at this". Then you wrapped it carefully in newspaper, put it in that carrier bag of yours and transported it, at great expense I'm sure, halfway across London. Now, I think that is quite remarkable. Don't you?'

'Well ... I ... I suppose . . . ' the hopelessly overpowered little man stuttered to a halt and offered no further resistance.

'When I called my assistant, Mr Baron, I did so because it is such an unusual thing to have such an awful thing delivered up for our delectation.'

'Well ... I ... I just . . . ' offered the owner, in the mildest of protests.

'No, no, don't apologise,' Bernard Thornton rolled on like a minesweeper, 'don't apologise, but *do* tell me why.'

'Why?'

'Why.'

'Why what?'

'Why you thought it was worth bringing it to us. I mean, just what is it about this grotesque little offering that led you to believe it might be of value?'

Like a rabbit hypnotised by a stoat, the man made no

113

attempt to fight back. Instead, he just fidgeted and fiddled with the buttons on his raincoat.

'Well,' he began, looking down at his plastic shoes in an attempt to avoid Thornton's gaze. 'I just thought it might be old.'

'You just thought it might be old,' Bernard Thornton repeated, slowly and deliberately, putting great emphasis on the final word. 'I see. But did you like it?'

'Like it?'

'Yes, you know did you look at it at any stage and think – my goodness, that's a pretty little vase!'

'No, I don't think so.'

'I see. So, basically what happened was that you looked at it, thought it was ugly but old, and as such might be valuable. Is that about the size of it?'

'Yes, I suppose so, but . . .'

'Interesting, very interesting. Fatally flawed of course. Doubly so, in fact, since this particular piece isn't old anyway. But even if it were so, something this awful just couldn't conceivably be worth anything; could it?'

'Well . . . I . . .'

'I mean, could it?' Once again Bernard Thornton beamed condescendingly at the man.

'I suppose not.'

'No, of course it couldn't. I mean, if a thing only needed to be old and ugly to be of value, then I'd be worth a fortune!' At this Thornton let out a strange, snorting braying laugh quite unlike anything I'd heard before.

Caught by surprise, the raincoated figure stumbled back a pace or two again.

'Always look first for quality,' Bernard Thornton continued. 'Never mind how old it is. Is it good? Isn't that right, William?'

William Baron, who had been standing by, expressionless, throughout the one-sided exchange, nodded sagely. 'Oh, yes, absolutely,' he confirmed.

His boss turned back to the crumpled figure in the crumpled raincoat. 'Now don't be depressed,' he instructed the unfortunate man, 'for all is not lost.' He reached out, picked up another item from the counter and held it up for its owner to see. 'Now, do you like this?' he asked.

'Yes – I think so,' the man replied nervously, clearly not keen on setting himself up for another exposé of his dubious taste and resultant inability to separate wheat from chaff.

'Good, I'm glad, because I think this is delightful.'

The piece in his hand was a balluster shaped porcelain mug painted with sprays of flowers. It was about six inches high.

'Do you know what it is?' Bernard Thornton asked.

Its owner shook his head, probably in the belief that if he remained silent, Thornton wouldn't humiliate him any further.

'It's Worcester, probably circa 1765, and, as I said, quite delightful. I suppose it would make a hundred and fifty to two hundred and fifty pounds under the hammer. Would you like us to sell it for you?'

'Well, yes, I think so.'

'Excellent! Mr Baron, here, will take all the details and give you a receipt. Thank you so much for bringing it in. Good morning.' He shook the man's hand vigorously for a moment, detaching himself without warning, and thereby leaving it waggling about in mid-air. 'Can I help you?' he boomed, looking across at me.

Bailey's saleroom was situated in a none too pretty sidestreet in down-town Twickenham. Even from the outside it had an air of Dickensian dilapidation about it which suggested that Charlotte's warnings were not quite as far-fetched as I had originally assumed. I sat in my car and looked out at the decaying structure.

115

Whatever it held, it was unlikely to be any more startling than the morning so far. I was still a little dazed from my first encounter with Bernard Thornton; and who wouldn't be? To have witnessed his unique handling of the man in the raincoat was an educational experience of inestimable value. That he could speak to him in the way he did, and yet still get the only item of any value in for sale, suggested a very polished performer. I could appreciate why Charlotte and Philip had been reluctant to come down firmly on whether his eccentricity was natural or cultivated. Whichever it was, it obviously gave him a considerable edge in negotiations, since the opposing party could never be sure what he was going to do or say next. He had been the epitome of charm when William Baron had introduced us and had readily agreed to look at Mrs Randolph-Bruce's porcelain. I just hoped Mrs Randolph-Bruce was up to it.

The squeaking front door to Bailey's auction galleries admitted me to a large T-shaped room packed with everything from old gas cookers to some half-reasonable furniture. It was scruffy, dirty, cold and absurdly congested. The furniture lots were stacked in long, uneven rows with only the narrowest of gangways between them. Consequently, just to get past one another, the people viewing the sale were forced into positions of intimacy not usually associated with auction rooms. Several porters with brown aprons seemed to be busy trying to locate specific lots for interested parties, although I got the impression they were being less than a hundred per cent successful. All in all it appeared to be an absolute shambles.

'Excuse me,' I said to one of the aproned figures as he sped past me, 'I'm looking for Harry Sutton.'

'That's me, sir. I'll be with you in one minute.'

I don't think he even looked at me as he spoke. He just pressed on, nose in catalogue, weaving his way through furniture and people at breakneck pace. As the dapper grey-haired figure disappeared into the general mêlée, I wasn't at all sure I would ever see him again.

I was wrong to doubt him. Harry Sutton was a man of his word, and in a few moments he popped up in front of me again like a piece of flotsam thrown up on the beach.

'Now, sir,' he said, brightly, 'how can I help you?'

I started to explain who I was but I wasn't allowed to finish.

'Mr Harton!' he exclaimed, with what appeared to be a combination of genuine enthusiasm and relief. 'I'm glad to see you, sir. Oh, I *am* glad to see you.'

I was ushered into a small, filthy office littered with paper and dirty tea and coffee mugs. Harry Sutton opened a drawer in the desk and took out a specially bound catalogue.

'Here's the auctioneer's book,' he said, 'you have a wander round with it if you like, and have a look at the reserves, sir.'

'Thank you, Harry. I will.'

'Anything at all I can help you with, sir, you just give me a call.' He spoke quickly, like a man whose mind was already dealing with the next problem, but he smiled throughout and seemed to be at home with the chaos about him.

'Thanks, I will,' I said. 'By the way; is it always as crowded as that out there?'

'Yes, sir, sometimes worse.' His bright blue eyes sparkled behind his rimless glasses. 'In fact, it's not too bad this week.'

'I see,' I said, opening the door to return to the saleroom.

'May I ask you something, sir?' he said, looking momentarily serious.

'Of course.'

117

'It's just that Mr Derby said you're going to be our regular auctioneer now. Is that true?'

'I believe that's the general idea, yes.'

'Oh, thank goodness for that, sir. I mean, we shouldn't complain because Mr Derby only does it as a favour, but it will be wonderful to have the same auctioneer each week.'

'Good.'

'We just never knew what to expect,' he went on. 'Sometimes nobody would turn up at all, and on a couple of occasions they sent down a bloke from the accounts office.'

'Really?'

'Yes – he was a nice enough chap but he had no idea. No idea at all. And the things he said: I mean, I'm easy going, Mr Harton, but I don't think "are you bidding or do you just want to be excused?" is a proper way to talk to people.'

'No,' I said, 'no, I think you're right.'

'So, just as long as you know, sir: it will be nice to have somebody sitting up there who knows what he's doing.'

'Thank you, Harry. I'll certainly do my best for you.'

It was a fulsome tribute and vote of confidence considering I hadn't even taken my hammer out of my pocket yet. I set out to inspect the sale, bathed in the warm glow of appreciation.

Viewing a Bailey's sale seemed to require not only a special technique but also considerable tenacity. The crush of people in the narrow rat runs between the stacks made any form of sustained forward progress impossible, while, in such close encounters, innocent accessories like briefcases and umbrellas became transformed into offensive weapons. So much so as to make the simple act of bending down to inspect something too hazardous to be worth seriously considering.

These difficulties were compounded by there being

118

no apparent order or system involved in the way the pieces were displayed. On top of that, many of the catalogue descriptions were so economical as to be very nearly meaningless: 'a mahogany table' and 'a chair and one other, similar,' didn't really give me much of an idea what to expect. However, one entry, described as 'A rosewood table, length 4ft.' did catch my eye. What puzzled me was that it wasn't catching my eye in the saleroom. It shouldn't have been too difficult to locate, but I could not find it anywhere.

I fought my way over to one of the brown-aproned figures. He was a roly-poly man with a head as polished as a billiard ball, and he was surveying the scene with a placid, if somewhat detached, gappy, benign smile.

'Excuse me,' I said.

'Yessir.'

'I'm looking for Lot 127 but I can't seem to find it.'

'Lot 127 . . . Lot 127 . . . Lot 127 . . . ' he muttered as he thumbed through his catalogue.

'It's a table,' I added, 'supposed to be four foot long. It should be big enough to see.'

'Ah . . . that one . . . yes . . . Lot 127 . . . that one . . . mmm!' he stood there, studying the one line description as if it might yield up some vital pointer as to the table's whereabouts; then, still looking at his catalogue, he began to stroke his shiny pate and whistle. It was a quiet, hissing whistle produced by blowing through what remained of his front teeth. It was also completely tuneless.

'Do you know where it is?' I asked.

'Well . . . mmm . . . er . . . ' He looked up from the catalogue.

'Scuse me asking, sir, but are you Mr Harton?'

'Yes.'

'Oh, well, right then, sir. You just hold on here a minute and I'll see if I can't find it for you.'

'All right,' I agreed, and watched him head off

towards the office. A few minutes later he was back with Harry Sutton at his side.

'It was the table you wanted to see, was it, Mr Harton?' Harry asked.

'Yes, it's just that it says in the catalogue that it's rosewood, and I wondered what period it was. It's only estimated at fifty to a hundred pounds. I can't quite envisage what it's like.'

'Not old,' Harry replied, solemnly.

His colleague nodded in silent agreement.

'How old would you say?' I asked.

'Oh . . . phew . . . difficult to say . . .'

'Well, I think I'd better have a quick look at it anyway.'

'Right, sir. Whatever you say, Mr Harton. Follow me, it's up this way.'

I thought, just for a split second, that I saw Harry Sutton and his colleague exchange glances which spoke of mutual frustration.

'It's just along here, Mr Harton,' Harry said, as he led the way out of the saleroom into an area of what appeared to be storage bays. 'By the way, sir,' he continued, 'I haven't introduced you to Polly, my right hand man, have I?' He gestured to his rotund companion.

'No,' I said, shaking hands with the still smiling porter. 'Hello, Polly.'

'His real name's Arthur – Arthur Porter,' Harry Sutton went on, 'but he's been Polly as long as I've known him, and that's the better part of forty years.'

'Your surname's Porter?' I said. 'That's appropriate.'

'Yes,' Polly grinned, 'Porter by name, porter by trade.'

Harry Sutton drew close to me and dropped his voice. 'He can be a bit deaf, but he's all right today – he's got his hearing aid turned up.'

In the last of the bays stood a stack of general furniture with half a dozen large rolls of carpet leaning against it.

'There we are, Mr Harton,' Harry Sutton said, 'that's the one.'

I wondered what it was Harry could see that I couldn't.

'Yes, of course, that's the one – Lot 127,' Polly Porter agreed, once again checking the catalogue description, perhaps to see if it had got any longer since he last looked at it.

'Yes, there it is,' Harry added, for good measure.

'This may seem a silly question,' I said, 'but, where is it?'

'What?' Harry asked, looking puzzled.

'The table, Harry,' I said. 'Where is the table? I can't see it.'

'Why, it's just there, sir, look,' Harry Sutton said, squatting down and pointing vaguely toward the centre of the bottom of the stack.

'Yes, Mr Harton,' Polly Porter added, getting down, rather unsteadily, on one knee, 'there it is, look – just in under there, next to the wardrobe.'

I got down on my hands and knees and looked deep into the stack of furniture. I could just pick out something that might have been a part of a table, but I wasn't sure. I looked at my watch: fifteen minutes to eleven.

'I'm sorry, Harry,' I said, 'I want to have a proper look at it. I really can't see what it's like from here.'

Harry Sutton and Polly Porter exchange sidelong glances very similar to those I thought I'd seen before. This time I was in no doubt as to their meaning: they were beginning to regard me as a considerable inconvenience.

'Yes, sir,' Harry replied, grin firmly back in place. 'We'll see to it right away. Polly, get Dave to give you a hand to break down that stack.'

I continued viewing the rest of the sale while Polly and his helper went about the disinterment of the table. Dave Williams, the young porter involved, showed far less enthusiasm for my arrival on the scene than had

121

either of his more senior colleagues. He acknowledged me with a cursory nod, and responded to Polly's news about the table with an observation long on passion and short on syllables.

With just five minutes to go before the start of the sale, I was summoned back to the storage bays by Harry Sutton.

'There we are, Mr Harton. That's the one,' he said.

The table he pointed to was indeed rosewood and about four foot in length. What the catalogue had failed to mention, however, was that it was also brass-inlaid and dated from about 1815.

'It's Regency,' I said, as I looked at it.

'What's that, sir?' Harry Sutton asked, innocently.

'It's Regency.'

'Regency! Well, there's a turn up for the book,' he said. 'Regency! Well I'm blowed.'

'Yeah! Well I'm blowed!' echoed Polly Porter, in a manner so stilted it sounded as though he was reading from a script.

'It's not in the best of condition,' I went on, 'but it's very good quality.'

'Well, I can see that now you mention it, sir,' Harry Sutton said. 'Can't you, Polly?'

'Oh, yeah,' Polly replied, 'now Mr H has pointed it out, it's clear as day.'

'Yes,' Harry agreed. 'Clear as day. You certainly know your stuff, Mr Harton – doesn't he, Dave?'

Dave Williams mumbled something and stared at the floor.

I looked at my watch: I was already five minutes late starting the auction. I'd discovered an under-catalogued piece of furniture hidden away in the store when it should have had pride of place in the saleroom, and something told me I was not the only one there who knew it was worth somewhere in the region of two thousand pounds.

I looked at the owner's name in the auctioneer's book. It meant nothing to me.

'Who does it belong to?' I asked.

'It's a probate lot, Mr Harton,' Harry said. 'Put in by a local firm of solicitors. No reserves or anything.'

'Do you know if we're holding any bids on it?'

'Er . . . let me just check . . . ' Harry Sutton scanned his catalogue. 'Cor, well, as it happens I have got one, Mr Harton.'

'I wouldn't usually ask, Harry,' I said, 'but, how much?'

He hesitated, then capitulated. 'Five hundred quid, sir – and do you know, I don't even remember being given that bid.'

'Right, if we don't get anything better than that I'll buy it in,' I said. 'It's not enough money.'

This time the looks were exchanged by all three porters, and I felt that Dave Williams had a particularly venomous glint in his eye.

'Er . . . ' Harry Sutton hesitated, stroked his chin and looked serious, ' . . . but there's no reserve on it, is there?'

'There is now,' I said, 'I've just put it on. I'll clear it with the owners later. I'm not going to stand by and watch one of your clients lose fifteen hundred pounds when I'm on the rostrum. Not now I'm the *regular* auctioneer.'

Dave Williams groaned audibly and turned away, but Harry Sutton maintained his outwardly unflappable demeanour.

'That's right, sir. You start as you mean to go on,' he said, then added, 'Isn't that right, Polly?'

Polly Porter made no reply. He hadn't heard the question. He'd turned off his hearing aid a few moments earlier.

'Well, how did you get on?' Charlotte asked when I arrived back at the office.

'All right, when it came to the sale itself – that was fun.'

'Oh, were there problems otherwise?'

123

'You could say that. I suspect the loyal staff at Bailey's Salerooms are at this moment fashioning a waxen effigy of yours truly, to which, in due course, they will do unspeakable things.'

'Goodness! What have you done to deserve that.'

'I think I probably cost them a lot of money, but I can't be sure.'

I recounted the story of the Regency table.

'What do you think they were up to?' Charlotte asked.

'Well, they might not have been up to anything. They might really have been ignorant of what it was, as well as having no idea of its true value.'

'But they knew about the five hundred pound bid on it, and they had it hidden away where nobody could see it. How did they explain its not being on view?'

'They started with "lack of space" but switched to "administrative cock-up". They shouldn't have done that. Both explanations were vaguely plausible, but not at the same time.'

'So, they were almost certainly involved in some sort of fiddle?'

'The facts would bear that interpretation,' I said.

'But what were they going to do with the table?'

'One of two things, I suppose. They could either buy the thing themselves and sell it on; or they could tip off a tame dealer who would buy it cheap and then, in due course, show his appreciation for all the help they'd given him.'

'Which do you think it was?' Charlotte asked.

'Oh, I suspect it was the latter. That way there would be no obvious involvement on their part. The accounts would all look right and proper. It would just be one more item that a dealer had spotted, but which an auctioneer had failed to recognise.'

'But, wouldn't the owner have noticed the table wasn't on view?'

'No. He's a local geriatric solicitor who never sets foot

in the saleroom. He'll probably be annoyed at the extra work I'm creating for him.'

Charlotte shook her head. 'What are you going to do about the porters?' she asked.

'Nothing.'

'Nothing? But you must do something.'

'Fine. What do you suggest? According to Bob Derby, Donald Bailey – the owner of the salerooms – is about a hundred and fifty and paralysed by a stroke. He hasn't been seen in the rooms for over five years, and almost certainly never will be again. He's had a succession of managers, each one of whom lasts for about three months, but the person who actually runs the place is Harry Sutton.'

'So?'

'So do you really think it would be a good idea to suggest to Mr Bailey that he sacks his entire workforce and closes down?'

'Oh, I see what you mean,' Charlotte said. 'But you must do something.'

'Yes, I will – I'll keep an eye on them.'

'What good will that do?'

'Quite a lot. It's been too easy for them over the last few years. From now on, if they want to fiddle, they're going to have to be a lot more ingenious than they have been in the past.'

She looked a little sceptical, then obviously remembered something. 'Talking of being ingenious,' she said, 'how about a nice cup of real coffee?'

'You managed to get a percolator? Well done. Where did it come from?'

'I can't reveal my sources I'm afraid.'

'You should do a couple of weeks at Bailey's,' I said, 'you could teach them quite a lot.'

Chichester Court was a large, red brick block of expensive flats. Built immediately after the Second World War, it was architecturally uninteresting but well placed geographically. As he'd promised, Messrs Hallworth, Jolly and Phillimore's Mr Parkinson was waiting for me just inside the plate glass main doors. He hadn't sounded a bundle of fun over the telephone, and he didn't look one either.

His face was lean and pinched, his expression rather superior. I made a few mental calculations as we ascended in the lift, and came to the conclusion that it would take a considerable chunk of my annual income to dress like Mr Parkinson. He was absolutely immaculate. From his velvet-collared overcoat to his dazzlingly polished black brogues, he was every inch the correctly turned out professional man. As for his natural choice of auctioneers, I had no doubt who he usually retained: he was a Christie's person if ever I saw one.

The bell pinged as the doors slid open at the fifth floor.

'It's along here, I think,' he said, turning right as we left the lift, 'number five hundred and seventeen.'

Outside the door to flat five-one-seven he stopped and drew two keys from his pocket. They were on a dirty piece of frayed string, along with a dog-eared label. He appeared not to be at home handling them. The whole business was clearly well below his normal level of operations. He undid the first lock then paused before he turned the second key.

'I understand it's a bit of a mess,' he said.

I nodded.

'You know the sort of thing,' he went on, 'old person, not able to cope – that sort of thing.'

'I understand,' I said.

'I haven't been here before, but one of my juniors returned to the office with a somewhat overdramatic and grisly account after he'd visited it last week. It's supposed to be pretty scruffy inside.'

126

'I'm sure I've seen worse,' I said, as he eventually turned the key and pushed open the door.

Mr Parkinson took one step into the flat and stopped dead in his tracks. 'Good God!' he said. 'What's that dreadful smell?'

I didn't know. I wondered for an instant whether it might be Mr Parkinson's late client, but dismissed the idea as fanciful. Whatever it was, it was horrible. I began to suspect that flat five-one-seven held secrets I had no wish to uncover.

Parkinson hovered on the threshold. 'What *is* that *dreadful* smell?' he repeated, his voice rising in apprehension.

'I don't know,' I said, looking over his shoulder and trying not to breathe in.

The door opened onto a small, dark lobby. There was a dirty-looking mirror on the wall in front of us, with one door to the left and another to the right. Mr Parkinson fumbled inside for the light switch. I heard it click on and off several times but nothing happened.

'Damn it! The electricity's off,' he said.

'Never mind. There should be enough light in the main rooms,' I replied. 'I'm sure the place has plenty of windows.'

'Yes, and the sooner we get some of them open, the better.'

Despite his words, he still hovered, nose twitching, in the lobby. Although I had no great desire to explore the place further, the job had to be done and we weren't going to do it by standing in the doorway.

'Perhaps we could start in the drawing room,' I suggested.

'Yes, yes, of course,' he said, 'let's get it over with.' He turned the handle of the door on his right and pushed it ajar.

The room was pitch black, but enough light spilled through from the open front door for us to be able to

127

identify it as an extremely primitive and very dirty kitchen.

'My God!' Mr Parkinson said, slowly. 'This is absolutely dreadful.' He drew back from the kitchen, turned around, and looked with some alarm at the remaining closed door. Then he took a deep breath, reached out, and opened the door. A moment later we were back in the corridor outside the flat. Our retreat from number five-one-seven had been less than orderly. I'd had little option but to withdraw, since if I had tried to hold my position I would have been knocked to the floor and trampled on by my suave companion. Not that he looked particularly suave now. He was leaning back against the wall with an immaculately laundered white handkerchief pressed against his nose and mouth. His forehead was grey and moist, and his eyes stared rather wildly. I could appreciate how he felt. Even I had suffered a slight wave of nausea, and whereas I'd seen some pretty bad places in my time, it was fairly clear that this was a whole new experience for the man from Hallworth, Jolly and Phillimore.

'Oh, God, it's absolutely disgusting in there,' he eventually managed to say. 'What on earth are we going to do?'

'Get back in there and get the place opened up,' I said. 'We haven't even seen what we're up against yet.'

'Yes, I suppose you're right. But give me a moment, I really feel quite ill.'

'All right, you take your time, but I'll get started.'

I left Mr Parkinson in the corridor, still leaning against the wall and staring into space. He really seemed incapable of movement. In the flat, by the light filtering through from outside, I carefully picked my way across the room until I felt the curtains in front of me. I drew them back, tore down the brittle, discoloured net curtains, and threw open the two large windows. I stuck my head out into the cold afternoon air and gulped it in in large mouthfuls. Five floors below, Belgravia went about its business, unaware of the mini-drama going on above it.

I looked about me at the room. I had been wrong earlier when I'd said that I would almost certainly have seen worse. I hadn't. The place was in an appalling state. It looked as though it had been inhabited by an animal, not a human being. Most of the furniture was broken and that which wasn't was heavily soiled with faeces and urine. As I surveyed the wreckage, Mr Parkinson made a rather shaky entrance into the room.

'Oh, my God!' he said, as he took in the scene. 'This is absolutely awful. I've never seen anything like it . . . never!'

'Did you know the deceased?' I asked.

'I'd met her on a couple of occasions, but that was years ago. I remember that her sight was failing her then, but otherwise she was fine.'

'Well, she wasn't by the time she died.'

'No, but there was no need for this,' he said, gesturing around him. 'She wasn't badly off; not rich, but certainly no shortage of money.'

'Any children?'

'No, although she had once been married – she was widowed during the war I believe. As far as I know there's just one nephew who lives in Australia. He's the sole beneficiary, anyway.' He looked round the filthy room again with utter disgust. 'But how could any human being live like this?' he asked.

'I don't know. Although, if you're blind, doubly incontinent, very old and alone in the world, I suppose it's easier to give up the struggle than it is to keep fighting.'

My answer didn't seem to impress my client. I'm not sure he even heard what I said. He just continued to regard the scene with a look of abject horror and disgust.

He started to cross the room towards me but he had

been standing in the same place for too long. The rug he was standing on was now quite firmly attached to the sole of one of his shoes. As he lifted his foot the rug came with it.

'Oh no! . . . how disgusting . . .!' After some moments spent staring helplessly at the floor, he eventually placed his other foot on the very edge of the rug so as to hold it down, then carefully peeled the offending object from his shoe. As he secured his release, his face betrayed that it was all becoming too much for him. Not only was the look of revulsion once again apparent, the moist pallor was also returning.

'Are you all right?' I asked.

'Actually, I don't feel too good. I think I'd better sit down,' he said.

'Well, I don't advise it – not in here anyway.'

He looked at the choice of seating available and recoiled. 'Oh, my God!'

'Why don't you wait for me outside, or down in the foyer,' I suggested. 'This shouldn't take me more than about twenty minutes.'

'Er . . . really I should remain and . . . er . . . and . . .' he faltered, then stopped. It was clear that while the professional spirit was willing, the aristocratic stomach was weak. 'Perhaps I will wait outside, if you don't mind, Mr Harton.'

'No, that's fine – you go ahead.'

'Thank you. I'll be just outside the door if you need me.'

'Fine.'

I knew why he'd been reluctant to leave me alone. He had wanted to keep an eye on me. It wasn't altogether unreasonable since, of course, he'd used neither me nor Hampson's before. But, somehow, I still felt a little insulted. I was quite sure that he wouldn't have found it necessary to breathe down the neck of a Christie's valuer.

'You're becoming far too sensitive,' I told myself.

'Stop moaning and get on with it.'

I began a systematic search of the flat. It was obvious from the outset that ninety-five per cent of the furnishings would have to be destroyed. There were two small Victorian tables which were saleable, and one chair which, once stripped of its upholstery, would also be fit to sell. Otherwise, most of the other furniture was suitable only for a bonfire. The gruesome little kitchen contained bits and pieces of utilitarian crockery and glass, and there were a few ornamental items scattered throughout the flat although most of them had been broken and badly repaired. Both the bedroom and bathroom held horrors greater than those of the drawing room and therefore received only the most cursory inspections. As a result, the valuation was completed less than fifteen minutes after Mr Parkinson had made his wobbly way out into the clean air of the corridor. But was it complete?

There were two things I hadn't come across in flat five-one-seven. It was possible I hadn't found them because they simply just were not there, but my instinct told me otherwise. In every probate valuation I had ever carried out I'd *always* found one of the items, and usually both.

The thing I usually found was something, anything, that was out of place: just some individual item that one wouldn't have expected to find there. It wasn't always of great value, although it did sometimes eclipse the rest of the valuation. I had never forgotten, years earlier, being asked to value the contents of a tied cottage in Sussex, following the death of the old retired gardener who had lived there. It was clean, tidy and well cared for, but there was nothing in it of any value at all. I was about to go when I decided to have just one more look around. It was then that I found a parcel hidden under the spare bed. It was long, wrapped in brown paper and covered in dust. Inside it was a Kazakh rug in perfect condition.

It probably dated from about 1880, and its geometrical pattern was picked out in the typical, strong reds, blues and ivory associated with rugs from the Caucasus. It made over seven hundred pounds, more than the rest of the old man's estate put together, and I never learnt how he came by it.

Then there was the other missing item. The one I'd found on each and every probate valuation I had ever carried out. The article was that humble hallmark of modern dentistry, the set of dentures. At some point, and often in the most unlikely piece of furniture, I would open a drawer or lift a lid and there they'd be grinning up at me. I'd found them in sideboads, workboxes, tea caddies, toilet mirrors, chests of drawers and jewel boxes, but so far I hadn't found them at flat five hundred and seventeen, Chichester Court. I was convinced they were there somewhere. Of course, they weren't important in themselves, but if I'd missed them, I might just have missed something else far more important, like a Kazakh rug for instance. It was no good, I had to have one more quick search.

I found the false teeth first. They were carefully wrapped in cotton wool and stored in a small cardboard box in a rusty old meat safe on the floor in the corner of the kitchen. Why I hadn't looked there before, I just don't know. The other missing piece was a bit more difficult to locate. But it was there.

In the bedroom, there stood a particularly nasty Victorian wardrobe. It was over seven feet tall, which left a gap of just a few inches between the top of its heavy moulded cornice and the ceiling. It also had an irritating habit, in that every time I walked anywhere near it, one of its weighty mirrored doors would swing open and crash against the old bedstead which stood in the middle of the room. Having avoided being pinned between the door and the bed, I began a careful search of the contents of the wardrobe. It had obviously not been used on a daily basis for a very long time. The clothes hanging inside were old and covered in dust. Towards the back, hanging in a plastic bag brittle with age, were the moth-eaten remains of an ancient mink coat which disintegrated when I touched it.

Most of the drawers were empty but for old lining paper, although a few still held yellowing linen and oddments. There was definitely nothing of value there, and since it was the last piece of furniture in the place, it seemed that my instinct had failed me after all. There really wasn't anything worthwhile in that smelly little flat.

I closed the wardrobe door and caught sight of myself in the flaking silvered mirror. In the excitement of the hunt I had got thoroughly covered with the accumulated filth of decades. I was smudged, smeared and dusty. My hands were black and my overcoat needed cleaning. What would Mr Parkinson think? I don't know what made me look up at that moment, but for some reason I glanced once more at the deep cornice which crowned the wardrobe. Its exceptional depth was probably chiefly responsible for the piece's overall exceptional ugliness, and as I stood there looking at it, I calculated that there must be a cavity eight or nine inches deep behind it.

I climbed up on a very rickety dressing stool and tentatively put my hand over the top of the cornice. I felt around blindly in the disgusting, soft, oily grime – nothing. Then I touched something. What was it? It wasn't paper. Cloth perhaps? Then I felt string. It was some sort of package. It wasn't very big, so I pulled it to the front of the wardrobe and carefully lifted it over the cornice. It was uneven in shape and, judging from its condition, had been up there for a very long time. I cleared some general debris from the top of the chest of drawers which stood next to the open window, and set the bundle down.

For a moment I savoured the thrill of anticipation, then I tugged at the string. It fragmented to leave just the dirty cloth wrapper. Gently, I folded it back to reveal another parcel. This time it was packaged in a yellow sheet of newspaper. Under the newspaper was one last protective piece of cloth. I opened it out and looked at the item it had concealed.

The earliest kovsh was a simple, Russian, wooden drinking vessel. Made and used by Slav peasants, it was little more than a ladle with a boat-shaped bowl and raised handle. As time went on, however, kovski ceased to be of any practical use, and by the end of the eighteenth century were being made in precious metals for presentation as awards. By the end of the nineteenth century, Fabergé and the other leading Russian silversmiths of the day were producing elaborately dec-orated examples in brightly coloured and delicately shaded enamels. Such was the thing that I had dis-covered skulking on top of the wardrobe in that filthy, squalid, little flat. And I was the only person alive who knew of its existence.

I bundled it back into its inner wrapper, closed up the windows of the flat, and went to find Mr Parkinson. He was standing looking out of the window at the end of the corridor.

'Ah, there you are,' he observed. 'I thought you were never coming. Let's get out of here. I've got some real work to do this afternoon.'

It seemed he was quite back to his old self. It was a pity; I'd preferred him when he was feeling nauseous.

'I've been thinking about this place,' he said, as we walked towards the lift. 'Strictly speaking, I'm instructed to put it all in store, but obviously that's out of the question.'

'Yes,' I agreed.

'So, is any of it saleable?'

'Three or four pieces, yes.'

'Could you sell them for me?'

'Not at Hampson's, no, but I could arrange for another auctioneer to take them for you.'

'Who?'

'Bailey's, in Twickenham. They take the residue of most of the estates we handle.'

'What about the stuff that can't be sold?'

'I'll arrange for them to dispose of it.'

'Will they do that?'

'Oh, yes. They'll clear the flat completely, although you should probably get the local health people in to fumigate it afterwards.'

'I was going to do that anyway,' he said, as we arrived at the lift. 'But I can leave all the other arrangements with you, then, can I?'

'Yes,' I said, 'but there is one other thing, Mr Parkinson.'

'What's that?'

'This,' I replied, smartly unwrapping my find and offering it to him.'

'What is it?' he asked, drawing back a little, manifestly fearful of touching anything that might have come from his late client's home.

I explained all about the kovsh and where I'd found it.

'Could it be Fabergé?' he asked, overcoming his aversion to the piece.

'No, but it was made in Moscow around 1900,' I said, 'and although I'm no authority on Russian silversmiths, I think the maker might by Fyoder Ruckert.'

'Is he good?'

'Well, put it this way: Hampson's would be very happy to offer it for you.'

'What's it worth?' he asked.

'A thousand to fifteen hundred pounds,' I said, 'perhaps more.'

'I see.' He stood looking at it as the lift arrived and the

135

doors opened. 'I'd better hold onto it for the moment until I've contacted the beneficiary, but I can't imagine he'd want to keep it.'

I nodded.

'Anyway,' he concluded, 'I'll let you know.'

I returned to the office, soiled but satisfied. If Parkinson didn't recognise what I'd done that afternoon as being well above and beyond the call of duty, nothing would impress him. I had undertaken the valuation at exceptionally short notice, risked picking up some very unpleasant diseases, got him out of trouble by getting Bailey's to clear the place, and displayed both tenacity and unswerving honesty when it came to the discovery of the kovsh. What more could he ask for?

I washed and tidied as well as the office facilities would allow, and then made a telephone call.

'Hello, Bailey's of Twickenham,' the voice on the other end chirped.

'Hello, Harry,' I said, 'it's Richard Harton.'

'Hello, sir. Nothing wrong is there?'

'No, Harry, nothing wrong. In fact I've got a little job for you.'

'Oh, fine, sir. Is it a nice juicy one?'

'Well, that's not quite the adjective I· would have chosen, Harry. Let me tell you all about it . . .'

Mr Parkinson never contacted me about the kovsh. Hallworth, Jolly and Phillimore settled our fee a little over two months after my visit to Chichester Court, the cheque being accompanied by a short, standard letter which made no mention of the fate of the piece. I assumed that, despite Parkinson's prediction, the Australian beneficiary had decided to keep it – and why not? After all, it was a nice thing and easily transportable to the other side of the world. Despite my disappointment, I couldn't blame him.

My views on both beneficiary and solicitor changed a

little some weeks later when I opened the catalogue on a forthcoming Christie's sale. I recognised the piece in the photograph immediately. There was no need to read the description.

I tossed the catalogue onto my desk and simmered in silence. Of course, it might have been the beneficiary who insisted that the kovsh be sold by Christie's. On the other hand, it might have been the duplicitous Mr Parkinson. The more I brooded on it, the more sure I became that the culprit was much closer to home than the Antipodes. In the end I harboured no doubts: Parkinson had taken me for a ride. All I could hope was that, one day, I might get the opportunity to treat him to a similar excursion. Until then, I just had to write it off to experience.

Chapter 10

I had barely got inside the door when Tom Morrison pounced.

'Thank God you're back,' he said. 'Where have you been?'

'Hampson's. Why? Where should I have been?'

'Nowhere – it's just that you're usually back earlier than this.'

I looked at my watch. It was a quarter past seven.

'I don't think so,' I replied, starting to unbutton my overcoat.

'Don't take your coat off,' he said, snatching up his own overcoat from the hall chair. 'We've got to leave right away. We're going to be late as it is.' As he spoke, he began to propel me backwards towards the still open front door.

'Hold on!' I complained. 'Leave for where? Late for what?'

'To meet the girls at the cinema of course! Now come on, Richard,' he went on, impatiently, as he bulldozed me across the threshold. 'I'll explain on the way.'

I clutched hold of the doorpost as it passed me by, and halted him for a moment. 'Will you please stop for a second!' I demanded, 'and tell me what on earth is going on.'

He hesitated then gave in. 'Oh, all right,' he moaned, 'but this'll have to be quick – basically I'm offering you a free and gratis introduction to a highly desirable and eligible young lady, all expenses paid – well, most of them, anyway. Now, can we please get going?'

'No.'

'Richard! You really can be a pain sometimes . . .'

'Who is she, and how come it's all so sudden?'

'Oh, God!' he raised his eyes to the heavens as he spoke. 'She's Catherine's cousin, and Catherine and I had arranged to go out this evening . . .'

'Catherine?' I queried.

'Yes, Catherine. You've met Catherine.'

'No, I've met Anne.'

'Oh!' he said, looking puzzled, 'that's odd. I was sure you'd met Catherine.'

'No,' I replied, 'I've definitely not met Catherine.'

'How strange. Never mind,' he continued undeterred, 'she's an absolute honey. You'll like her – but I'd appreciate it if you didn't mention Anne this evening, just in case.'

'No danger of that – I won't be there.'

'Don't be ridiculous, of course you'll be there – to look after Sally.'

'Who's Sally?'

An expression of intense annoyance registered temporarily on Tom Morrison's face, then it melted into a look of acute fatigue. 'Catherine's cousin of course.'

'Of course – silly me.'

'She's descended on Catherine from Welsh Wales for two days without warning . . .'

'Ah, now I get it!' I said. 'You need an escort for her, otherwise your date with Catherine's up the spout.'

'Discounting your totally inappropriate expression, in a word – yes. And since I've laboured long and hard to woo the fair Catherine, let's go.'

'Forget it.'

'Oh, come on, Richard,' he implored, tugging at my sleeve. 'You've got to help me. I've already told them you're coming. Anyway, what else have you got planned for tonight?'

'I've got to start packing.'

'Packing?'

'Yes, that flat I went for the other week – I've got it.'

'Well, thanks for letting me know,' he said, sarcastically.

'I only heard about it this morning, and since I haven't been able to get a word in edgeways since I got back . . .'

'Yes, yes,' he said, once again beginning to ease me out onto the front step. 'I'm sure I'm incredibly happy for you. But you don't have to start packing tonight – you've got next to nothing here as it is.'

'Well . . .'

'And I can help you pack tomorrow.'

'No, Tom. I really don't . . .'

'Richard! You must come! You owe me!' He almost shrieked the words. Obviously this date was a lot more important to him than I had realised.

'Owe you? What for?'

'Well . . . for . . . for pushing your bloody car the other morning for one thing . . . and . . . and . . . ' He cast about furiously for another unsettled debt. ' . . . and for giving you a roof over your head when you were homeless . . . and . . .'

'No more! No more!' I cried. 'I give in. It's just . . .'

'Just what?' he asked, brightening up immediately.

'Just that I hate blind dates.'

'Oh, Sally's not blind,' he replied brightly. 'A little myopic perhaps, but definitely not blind!'

During a hazardous, high-speed journey to the Fulham Road I managed to elicit from Tom the briefest of briefs on the arrangements for the evening ahead.

We were due to see a film, the title of which escaped him, followed by dinner in a nearby Italian restaurant, the name of which he couldn't remember.

140

'I don't expect there's any chance that you recall which cinema we're meeting them at?' I asked.

'Oh, yes,' came the confident reply. 'It's definitely the one in the Fulham Road. They'll be waiting for us in the bar. It'll be easy to spot them – they'll be under the table by the time we get there.'

They weren't, but it was still easy to identify them – they were the only people left in the bar. However, if I hadn't already been told they were cousins I would never have guessed. One was tall, willowy and very good looking, while the other was short, heavily built and blessed with a face which might most charitably be described as interesting. From the outset I had no doubt which of them was Sally.

'Morrison! Where have you been?' demanded the one who wasn't.

'Well, we had a bit of . . .'

'Everybody else has already gone in – the film's starting!'

'Yes . . . er . . . the problem was . . .'

'Oh, never mind!' she interrupted, her tone suggesting she minded very much. 'For God's sake let's get in there before they play the national anthem.'

'I don't think they do that anymore,' I said.

Two pairs of smouldering eyes immediately turned their incinerating gaze in my direction.

'Er, this is Richard,' Tom said with an inappropriate level of cheerfulness.

'Hello,' Catherine responded, curtly.

'Hi,' Sally sneered, obviously already convinced that her companion for the evening was mentally retarded as well as unpunctual.

'He's an auctioneer,' Tom persisted.

'Oh, good,' Catherine responded, icily. 'If we wait a little longer he'll be able to sell these tickets as antiques, won't he?'

Tom responded with a nervous laugh, then,

thankfully, pulled himself together: 'Right! What are we waiting for? Let's get in there!'

As it happened, the film was still trundling through a daunting footage of opening credits as we stumbled along behind the usherette's elusive, flickering torch beam to our seats.

In the periodic flashes of bright light which swept the screen I could see that the auditorium was all but full.

The gum-chewing girl stopped and shone her pallid light away to our right where our seats were just visible in the middle of the row. I calculated, in the alternate burst of white light and unfathomable darkness, that approximately fifteen to twenty members of the audience stood, or rather, sat between us and seats twenty-eight to thirty-two inclusive.

Tom led the way, followed by the two girls, with me bringing up the rear.

'I'm sorry . . . excuse me . . . excuse me . . . sorry . . . whoops!' We whispered, muttered, hissed and grovelled our way to our objectives.

'Oh, this isn't right, is it?' Tom observed on reaching our seats. 'You should have come in first, Catherine, then I'd be able to sit between you and Sally . . .'

'Shhhhh!' demanded somebody in the darkness in front of us.

'Sorry . . . look I'll just squeeze past you, and then . . . ' Tom continued undaunted.

'Will you please sit down!' This time the request originated behind us.

In the flickering light I observed Tom and Catherine go through a brief but athletic series of intimate contortions before they fell into their respective, new seats. Even in the semi-darkness it seemed clear to me that he was enjoying it far more than she was.

I have never been quite sure exactly what happened next, but as I stooped to put down my seat, and Sally lowered her own ample frame into hers, my right hand

142

struck something in the darkness. There was the unmistakable crash of the two rows of pearly-white teeth being brought together, then the utterance of a single expletive.

'I'm so sorry,' I whispered. 'Are you all right, Sally?'

'No, I'm not, you clumsy moron!' came back her not altogether forgiving reply. 'You nearly broke my jaw, you ... you ... ' Fortunately, at that point, words seemed to fail her.

'Sorry,' I mumbled.

'Shhhh!'

'Sorry,' I repeated to whoever it was doing the 'shushing' in front.

'Shhhh!' came back an angry chorus from all around.

'Oh, God!' This time it was my companion again.

'What?' I enquired in a hoarse whisper.

'I've lost my bloody contact lens! You've knocked out one of my contact lenses.'

'Which one?' I asked, as if it were likely to make some sort of difference.

'Oh, I don't know ... the right one, I think ... ' I got a brief view of her raising her hand to her left eye, then all was darkness again.

' ... yes, it's the right one – it's gone.'

'Can you see without it?' I asked.

'Of course I can't, you idiot,' she snarled. 'Why do you think I wear the bloody things in the first place?'

'Shhhh!'

'Oh, why don't you sod off!' she asked our invisible critic, who, suitably intimidated, made no reply.

'Do you have any glasses with you?' I asked.

'No.'

'What do you want to do, then?' I whispered, suddenly conscious that an early escape from this purgatory might be beckoning.

'You'll have to find it!' she hissed.

'What?'

143

'You'll have to find it!'

'How? I can't see my own hand in front of my face, let alone a contact lens. I mean – it could be anywhere.'

'Be quiet!' This time it was somebody behind us again.

'Oh, shut up!' I snapped.

'You'll have to get them to turn the lights up,' Sally continued, displaying the sort of self-confidence that can only result from centuries of landed privilege.

'You must be joking!'

'I'm bloody not – get out there and tell the manager. Now!'

It was the final 'Now!' that did it. I suppose the fear I felt was akin to that which soldiers feel when they're about to go over the top: more frightened of upsetting their sergeant-major than of being shot by the enemy. Meekly, I began the journey back to the aisle.

'Excuse me . . . I am sorry . . . sorry . . . excuse me . . . I do apologise . . .'

The manager was, suitably enough for one who spent so much of his working life in the dark, a pale, slight young man who patiently devoted considerable time to explaining why he couldn't stop the film. The reasons were legion, but by far the most convincing argument was that in the resulting riot, certainly one, or possibly both of us, would be lynched.

'How about lending me a torch?' I suggested.

'No problem. I'll get you one from the office.'

He returned a few moments later with an usherette's torch from which drizzled a faint beam of insignificant light.

'Good luck,' he said. 'This has happened several times, you know. Your're not the first.'

'Really? Did the others find their lenses?'

'Oh, no. It's quite hopeless,' he replied brightly.

'Excuse me . . . excuse me . . . I am sorry . . . excuse me . . . I do apologise . . . ' I made my way back to where our jolly little party was seated.

144

'Now,' I whispered in the darkness to the anonymous, lumpy form that I calculated must be Catherine's Welsh cousin, 'do you have any idea where it went?'

If nothing else, the purple profanity offered in reply to my polite enquiry confirmed that I had at least found my way back to the right seats. There couldn't have been two women in that audience with Sally's lyrical turn of phrase.

There seemed nothing else for it other than to get down on my knees and comb the carpet inch by inch. Slowly, and with some difficulty, I got down into the cramped narrow space between the rows of seating and turned on my glow-worm torch. There was almost no room at all to move but I carefully began to examine my surroundings for the errant eye-piece.

'Get your hand off my leg!' hissed Sally, after a few moments.

'But, I haven't touched your leg,' I whispered in protest. 'I'm just . . . Aaaah!'

'What the hell's the matter now?'

'You've got your foot on my hand!' I complained. 'Get your foot off my hand!'

She lifted her foot, and I prised my crushed fingers from the carpet.

'Well, just keep your grubby little paws to yourself,' she added, ungraciously.

'I swear I didn't touch you,' I replied angrily, as a snort of laughter escaped from Tom Morrison, leaving me in no doubt as to who had been responsible for the phantom grope.

'Shhhh!'

'Oh, sod off!' the four of us replied in unison.

For several more minutes I continued to quarter the horribly grubby carpet in the area of our seats. I discovered cigarette ends, chewing gum, matches and sweet papers, as well as some other pieces of twentieth century detritus that, until then, I hadn't thought of

145

linking with the cinematic arts. Nevertheless, fearful of the price of failure, I searched on.

'Oh, God!' I said, at length.

'Have you found it?' Sally enquired, shrill and expectant.

'No, I haven't,' I replied. 'I've knelt on a . . . ' I turned the torch beam on the cold, wet, soft object temporarily attached to my knee. ' . . . I've knelt on a Choc-Ice!'

'Well, stop buggering about and *find my contact lens!*'

That was it. I'd had enough. She could find her own bloody contact lens. I shuffled backwards out from under her seat and, still kneeling, shone my torch full in her face. 'Well, let me tell you what you can do with . . . ' I stopped – something in the torchlight had caught my eye.

In the heat of the cinema, Sally had one by one cast off her outdoor clothes, so that by then, her considerable bust was contained in nothing more substantial than a very low-cut, flimsy cotton top. It was there, just above the plunging neckline, nestling in her deep cleavage, that I saw it – like a single, glistening fish-scale stuck to her pink flesh. I turned the torch beam on it, and with a cry of triumph reached out my hand to claim the prize.

'Animal!' she shrieked, and unleashed a blow at the side of my head which made my original right hook look like a playful caress.

'Shhhh!'

'It was a shame Sally developed that headache and couldn't stay for dinner,' Tom observed as we drove back to Wandsworth.

'Yes, due to watching so much of the film with only one contact lens, I suppose,' I said.

'Mmmm, mind you, by rights, it should have been you with the headache – she packs a punch that could stop a rhino.'

'Yes, it was fortunate that the chap next to me took

the full force of the blow.'

'Yes, he wasn't too happy though – not that he could convey any emotion for some time.'

'No, too badly winded,' I agreed.

'Mmm, it certainly was one hell of a punch,' Tom mused as we drew up outside his house.

'Anyway, Tom,' I said, 'I'm sorry if I ruined your evening with Catherine.'

'Nonsense, she said she'd never laughed so much in her life. And you did her a great service for which she'll be eternally grateful, of course.'

'I did? What service was that?'

'You ensured that cousin Sally will never again drop in unannounced for the night.'

Chapter 11

'Drop me here, cabby.'

'What, guv?'

'Drop me here, please. It'll be quicker if I walk the rest.'

'Okay, guv. I reckon you're right – this traffic's bleedin' unbelievable this morning.'

I jumped out of the taxi, paid the driver and set off up Park Street at speed. I hated being late for appointments and loathed having to rush to keep them. My aim was always to arrive at my client's on the dot of the allotted hour, in a state of cool, calm, dignified professionalism. So, the prospect of pitching up ten minutes late in a breathless flurry of perspiration did not please me, especially since I had allowed so much time for the journey at the outset. On top of that, I was not the only representative of Hampson's due to call on Mrs Randolph-Bruce that morning. Bernard Thornton was supposed to be meeting me there, and at this rate he was going to beat me to it. That really was worrying.

Over the telephone, Mrs Edwina Randolph-Bruce had sounded quite frail and elderly, and the thought of her being subjected to the sort of interrogation I'd seen Thornton putting the man in the raincoat through was horrible. I re-doubled my pace and sprinted across Oxford Street as the lights changed. After all, things were beginning to look up at Hampson's now, so I could do without a disaster.

148

And looking up they were. On the previous evening I had moved most of my worldly goods into my new flat in Kensington, finally putting an end to the physical and mental torment which resulted from sharing a house with Tom Morrison and his merry band. On top of that, there was some work coming our way at last. Not that it was due to any brilliant marketing strategy of mine. It just seemed to be happening – and I was very grateful it was. However, it'd been just such an incoming piece of business that had delayed me that morning.

I was on my way down the office stairs when Charlotte called me back: 'It's a Sarah Bishop,' she said, 'about a large probate valuation near Colchester. I think you'd better talk to her. It sounds important.'

It was. Miss Bishop worked for MacGregor Roche and Partners, a firm of solicitors who, if they put a quarter of their probate work Hampson's way, would seriously increase our turnover. As with the solicitors handling the dreadful Chichester Court job, they had never used us before, but were driven to it now because nobody else could conform to their timetable. I made a provisional appointment to meet Sarah Bishop at the house the following day. It was left that she would call back during the afternoon to confirm the arrangements once she'd cleared them with the deceased's son, who also intended to be present.

'It could take me ages to find a meter anywhere near Mrs Randolph-Bruce's,' I said, checking my watch. 'I think I'd better play safe – I'll go there by cab.'

'I hope you get one,' Charlotte replied, 'it looks as though it's beginning to sleet out there.'

Charlotte was right, and as is the custom at the first sign of precipitation, the 'For Hire' lights went out all over London. Huddled down inside the collar of my overcoat, I set off to stalk a taxi.

To begin with, I could either walk north towards

Knightsbridge, or west towards Sloane Street in search of my prey. Since Sloane Street promised to be a happier hunting ground I set my face to the west. I am convinced that once one has made up one's mind to do something it is best not to look back – to do so is usually depressing. Foolishly, that morning, I made the mistake of glancing over my shoulder. At precisely that moment, a convoy of black cabs passed by the other end of Vanbrugh Street on their way to Knightsbridge. As they came and went, each cosy, dry vehicle mocked me with its brightly illuminated sign. I turned to the west again and cursed them through gritted teeth.

Then, forty yards ahead of me at the junction, I saw one. It was empty, just standing there with its bored driver waiting for the traffic lights to change.

One of my cardinal rules is: 'Never Run for Public Transport'. It goes back to my boyhood, and that humiliating red-faced sprint for the fast-receding schoolbus – an event which took place at least twice a term. It always seemed to me that the pleasure experienced by the watching passengers was directly proportional to just how tantalisingly close I got to catching the thing before it eventually accelerated away. As an adult I vowed I would never again be the unwilling source of so much amusement. But, what's a little sadistic pleasure for your fellow man when you've just spotted the only empty cab in SW1.

Coat flapping, arms waving, screaming like a banshee, I thundered up the street, side-stepping my fellow pedestrians with a technique that wouldn't have been out of place at Twickenham. I was within feet of my objective when, in a matter of seconds, an immaculate pin-striped figure stepped straight out from a doorway and into the taxi at the precise moment the lights changed. As the usurper was whisked away, I was left stranded in the middle of the road until the lights changed again.

I walked almost the entire length of Sloane Street

before I succeeded in finding a cab, and even that proved a hollow victory. The traffic was so heavy I eventually decided to abandon the transport which had evaded me for so long in favour of completing my journey as I'd begun it: on foot, at the gallop, in heavy sleet.

I don't believe I looked at all cool, calm or professionally dignified when Mrs Randolph-Bruce opened her door to me.

'Mrs Randolph-Bruce, I do apologise for being so late.'

'Oh, don't worry, Mr Harton. I've been having tremendous fun. Mr Thornton's been telling me all about my china. It's really very exciting; apparently, everything I thought was valuable is absolute rubbish and all the things I thought were rubbish are priceless. He's so amusing and *so* clever, I haven't enjoyed myself so much for years.'

I heaved a sigh of relief. It was my first real illustration of just how sure Bernard Thornton's touch was when it came to dealing with clients. He had a sort of second sense about just how far he could go, and he seemed to adjust his degree of eccentricity accordingly. I can't say I ever relaxed in his presence, but after Mrs Randolph-Bruce's valuation I never again worried that he might inadvertently sabotage one of my clients. He was far too much of a pro for that.

It was about an hour and a half after my arrival that he came and found me in the drawing room where I was busy listing the furniture.

'Richard, I've finished my side of the valuation. Do you need a hand?'

'Yes, please, Bernard. It'll only take about another half an hour if you can write for me.'

'Okay, then I'd like you to listen to a little tale of woe the old girl told me earlier. There's absolutely nothing we can do about it, but it's a good cautionary story for you to tell your grandchildren.'

'Well, it's like this, Mr Harton,' our client began, as we

settled down with our coffee. 'I have an old friend who lives in one of the neighbouring flats and I'm really quite concerned that she's being defrauded. I have no proof to that effect you understand, I just have a feeling that all is not as it should be.'

'I see,' I said. 'Well, you go ahead and tell me about it and I'll tell you what I think.'

Mrs Randolph-Bruce put down her coffee cup, sat back in her chair and began: 'My friend is almost eighty and not in very good health I'm afraid. She hasn't been able to get about too well for some time now, and apart from the odd visit to the hospital I don't think she's set foot outside her flat for at least three years. Like me, she's a widow, but she does have one daughter who comes and visits her every now and then. I have to say at this point that I do not like the daughter, and in fairness, it might be my dislike of her which is at the root of my suspicions.'

'I see,' I said, as Mrs Randolph-Bruce paused for a moment.

'My friend,' she continued, 'has what I always considered to be a large collection of snuff boxes. It had been put together by her late husband who was, I think, very knowledgeable about them. He was certainly obsessive about collecting them, to the extent that poor Kitty, my friend, had to stand by while over the years the collection gradually seemed to take over the entire flat.' She smiled but shook her head. 'I mean, I like nice things, Mr Harton, and some of them were quite beautiful, but they were everywhere, and I must confess I found them a terrible nuisance. Then, one day, about a year ago, I popped in to see her and realised something was different about the flat. Do you know, it was absolutely ages before I grasped what it was. It was the snuff boxes – there were nowhere near as many.'

'The Case of the Vanishing Snuff Boxes,' Bernard Thornton said, opening his eyes wide and grinning.

'Yes, that's right,' Mrs Randolph-Bruce laughed, 'straight out of Sherlock Holmes. As far as I was concerned it was an absolute mystery and particularly strange because Kitty made no mention of the missing boxes at all.'

'Did you ask her about them?' I said.

'Yes, Mr Harton. Yes, I did. Although only in a roundabout sort of way to begin with. You see, I thought she might be selling them secretly because she was hard up and didn't want anyone to know about it, so I just commented that I thought she'd moved them around. Do you know? She didn't even reply, just went on talking as though she hadn't heard me. And let me tell you, for all Kitty's afflictions, there's nothing wrong with her hearing.

'Anyway, each time I went to see her there seemed to be less and less snuff boxes about. At first it was just those which stood around in the open that were disappearing . . .'

'In the open?'

'Yes, Mr Harton, you know, just lying around on tables and chests and windowsills – as I said, they were everywhere – but then there were others, special ones, which were all locked away. Most of them in a rather pretty glass-topped display table which stood near the drawing room window. Now, there was one particular box in there which I had always admired. I know what it was because Dan – Kitty's late husband – told me all about it. He used to joke that he'd leave it to me in his will. It was Russian, made in Moscow in about 1800, and it was enamelled gold. Do you know the sort of thing I mean?'

'Yes, I do,' I said.

'It was rectangular with the most beautiful picture on the lid. It was some sort of harbour scene – I suppose that's what you'd call it – you know, lots of ships with billowing sails and so on.'

'It sounds very nice.'

'Oh, it was, Mr Harton. So when I saw it was missing I just asked Kitty outright what was going on. She tried to pretend she didn't know what I was talking about at first, then she just broke down in floods of tears. The poor dear had obviously made herself ill worrying about it, and once she started telling me what had happened I could see why. It was all the fault of that wretched daughter of hers. I just knew she was at the bottom of it somewhere.' Mrs Randolph-Bruce's colour rose as she spoke of her friend's offspring. She certainly hadn't exaggerated earlier when she'd said she didn't like the woman. I was beginning to get the distinct impression that she loathed her. In view of the fact that, otherwise, our client seemed mild-mannered and generous by nature, it was difficult not to conclude that Kitty's daughter was an out and out stinker.

'Would you like some more biscuits, Mr Thornton? I can easily get you some,' our narrator asked.

I looked across to Bernard to see that he had absent-mindedly devoured an entire plate of 'Rich Tea' and 'Ginger Nuts' while Mrs Randolph-Bruce had been telling her tale.

'No, no, dear lady,' he said, raising his hands in protest, 'please don't trouble yourself. I really shouldn't eat them anyway. Unfortunately, I can resist everything but temptation.'

'As long as you're sure.'

'Absolutely!'

'All right. Now where was I?'

'Your friend was about to explain what had happened to the snuff boxes,' I said.

'Oh, yes, that's right,' our client said, settling back into her chair again. 'Kitty's daughter changes her husbands with the same sort of frequency that most people seem to change their cars these days. She doesn't happen to have one at the moment, but according to her mother she's having some sort of a fling with an antique dealer

154

down on the south coast.' She sniffed hard to mark her contempt for either the daughter, the fling, the antique dealer, the south coast or possibly all four.

'On top of which,' she continued, 'she is perennially short of money and always running to her mother for help – typical only child: ruined her life by being spoilt at the beginning.' Mrs Randolph-Bruce sniffed her disapproval once more. 'Now, although Dan left Kitty comfortably off, she's not a rich woman by any means and she can't afford to keep dipping into her savings, so the daughter dreamed up a master plan.'

'She got her mother to sell the snuff boxes to the boyfriend?' I suggested.

'No, Mr Harton, more clever than that: she got the creature to sell them for her mother on commission. Bit by bit she's been stripping the collection, and every now and then Kitty receives a statement of what has been sold, along with a cheque for what it all came to after he'd taken his commission.'

'Does all the documentation tie in with what's been taken from the flat?' I asked.

'Kitty seems to think it does. But she's very confused about it all, and having seen one of these statements I'm not surprised.'

'What do you mean?'

'Well, the descriptions were so brief they don't really mean anything. They just said things like: "a tortoiseshell snuff box" and "a yellow metal snuff box"; hardly any dates or anything like that. I'm sure Kitty hasn't a clue which is which.'

'Well, it certainly doesn't sound very professional, I agree,' I said.

'No, Mr Harton, but I can't help thinking it's much worse than unprofessional. I think it's *crooked*.'

'You could be right,' Bernard commented, 'but as I said earlier it might have more to do with ignorance than dishonesty.'

155

'Bernard's right, Mrs Randolph-Bruce,' I said, 'if this chap was really intent on fiddling your friend, I would have thought he would have tried to get her to sell to him direct rather than going in for this commission sale arrangement. Do you know if he did try to buy them?'

'No, as far as I know it was never suggested, but, you see, Kitty's never even met him.'

'I didn't realise that,' Bernard said, looking a lot more suspicious. 'I'd assumed he'd visited your friend's flat and discussed the whole set-up with her.'

'No, no, it's all been arranged through the daughter.'

'How does she know which boxes to take?' I asked. 'Does your friend tell her which ones she wants to sell.'

'No, I don't think so. As I understand it, the daughter just chooses them at random.'

'Oh, dear,' I said.

'Oh, dear, indeed,' added Bernard.

We all sat in silence for a moment. As I saw it, there were two or three possible explanations for what was going on. The difficulty was in discovering which was correct and what, if anything, we could do about it.

'Is there any chance of seeing your friend and what remains of the collection?' I asked.

'No, I'm afraid not,' Mrs Randolph-Bruce replied. 'I did try to persuade her but she says she just isn't well enough to deal with all the upheaval involved.'

'There wouldn't be any upheaval,' I said.

'I know. I think it's just an excuse. I think she's frightened she might find out that her daughter's been systematically robbing her.'

'How about having a look at one of the statements?'

'She won't let them out of her sight. She only showed me because she was so upset.'

'Do you remember the name of the dealer?' Bernard asked.

'Oh, yes. I made a mental note of that all right – at least, I made a note of the name he trades under. It was

156

Harbour Antiques, Whitecliffe, Kent.'

'Good – well done!' my colleague said. He groped through his jacket pockets, eventually producing a pen and a battered cigarette packet. 'Harbour Antiques, Whitecliffe,' he repeated, scribbling down the name.

'Does that name mean anything to you?' the old lady asked.

'No! Never heard of it,' Thornton said, returning his pen and improvised notepad to his pockets, 'but I've got to go down to Kent in the next three or four weeks, and if I end up anywhere near Whitecliffe, I'll make a point of dropping into Harbour Antiques.'

'What about you, Mr Harton?' Mrs Randolph-Bruce asked. 'Have you ever heard of Harbour Antiques?'

'No, I haven't,' I said, shaking my head.

'Oh, dear, I don't know what to do,' Mrs Randolph-Bruce said. 'Poor Kitty has no idea what's going on, which box is which, which boxes have been sold, or which ones are still at this fellow's shop . . . she's worried sick about it . . . doesn't seem to be able to get any information out of her daughter . . .'

'And there's the rub,' my colleague cut in. 'I think you were quite right to identify the daughter as the villain of the piece. We may well be right in accusing Harbour Antiques of ignorance, incompetence, stupidity, lack of moral fibre, and the general inability to organise a drunken brawl in a distillery, but . . .' he paused, 'there is no indication they or he or whoever have done anything against the law. It is quite clearly the daughter who has organised all of this.'

'So you don't think there's anything that can be done?' our client asked, sadly.

'I doubt it,' I said, 'certainly not unless your friend's prepared to talk to me about it.'

'But I will look into Harbour Antiques if I possibly can,' Bernard added. 'And do, please, try to stop your friend from parting with what's left of the collection. It

157

might be possible to salvage something from the wreckage.'

'I'll try, Mr Thornton, and I'll try to persuade her to see you, Mr Harton,' Mrs Randolph-Bruce said. 'But I'm afraid the answer will still be no. It's just all such a shame – and all the fault of that selfish, grasping girl.'

Bernard Thornton eased his car into the maelstrom of vehicles hurtling round Marble Arch, then stamped the accelerator to the floor. We lurched forward into the path of an oncoming cab which just managed to take evasive action.

'Bloody shame about those snuff boxes, Richard,' he commented, either unaware of or unimpressed by what the taxi-driver had promised to do to him if they ever met under different circumstances.

'Yes, I don't see that there's anything we can . . . ' dry mouthed, I temporarily lost the power of speech as my side of the car steadily closed on a large, solid-looking red bus. My voice returned when the distance between the two vehicles had dwindled to something approaching a coat of sparingly applied silicone wax. 'Bloody hell!' I shrieked.

'What's the problem?'

'Nothing, Bernard, nothing,' I whispered as he nonchalantly spun the wheel to the opposite lock and veered off towards the northern end of Hyde Park, seriously inconveniencing several more motorists as he did so.

'I always enjoy driving through the park,' he said, 'and it's generally the quickest way.' He looked out towards the Serpentine. 'How are you finding your way around London, Richard? Had you done much driving in town?'

'No, I hadn't,' I replied, 'but I'm beginning to get used to it.'

'Yes, it's all a matter of confidence, and knowing where you're going of course.'

If, at that moment, Bernard had any idea where *he* was

going, it was pure chance since he hadn't troubled to look at the road ahead for some time. Had he done so he would have noticed a long queue of stationary vehicles waiting for the lights to change at the Alexandra Gate.

'Bernard, I think . . . ' I pointed, frantically, in the direction of the motionless column of motors.

'Mmmm? Oh!' Once again, he spun the wheel, this time just managing to swerve to the right of the car ahead.

I quite expected him to pull up, reverse back and join the queue, but Bernard Thornton was made of sterner stuff. He simply drove straight on past the waiting vehicles, largely on the wrong side of the road and apparently not one little bit concerned about what was going to happen when we arrived at the gate itself. About twenty yards away from that obstruction he flicked down the indicator, and with no further warning veered left, coming to an abrupt halt with his front bumper just inches away from one of the patiently waiting cars in the line.

I released my white-knuckle grip on the dashboard for a moment and took stock of the situation. If we were to succeed in muscling our way into the orderly convoy which we were currently menacing, it seemed to me that we were largely at the mercy of the brand new Jaguar to my immediate left. Slowly, and as inconspicuously as possible, I looked sideways at the man at the wheel. He did not look promising. He was staring straight ahead, trying hard to ignore our presence, while easing his car forward, bit by bit, almost imperceptibly reducing the distance between his Jaguar and the car in front to just a few millimetres. In response to this clear statement of territorial integrity, Bernard, also looking straight ahead, pulled his own car forward a few more inches. Not, however, in a single, smooth glide like the Jaguar, but in a series of erratic, intimidating lurches and jumps

159

which left me clinging to the dashboard again. Of course, encounters of this nature are merely man's version of the sort of stylised battles you get between males of various animal species in the wild. There's a lot of pacing about and posturing, a fair amount of noise, and occasionally heads get banged together; but seldom does anybody really get hurt. One of the two protagonists almost always gives way before serious damage is done. I glanced to my left at the stonefaced figure at the wheel of the Jaguar, then to my right at the wild eyes of my own flamboyant chauffeur, and wondered if it was too late to get out. It was: the traffic lights ahead were about to change to green.

'Stick your hand out of the window, Richard, indicate we're turning left, and at the same time smile and say "Thank you" to our friend,' Bernard instructed, as we began another intimidating forward thrust.

I cranked down my window, stuck my hand out, smiled into the steel-grey eyes in the Jaguar and mouthed the words. 'Thank you'.

'I don't think he's going to let us in, Bernard,' I said.

'Nonsense!'

'Have it your own way, but whatever it was he just said to me, it wasn't "after you, old chap".'

'Geronimo!' Thornton shrieked as the car immediately in front of us pulled away. We leapt forward again, towards the opening gap.

Distracted by me, the driver of the Jaguar was just a fraction slow off the mark, so by the time he'd got started, Bernard had succeeded in getting the nose of our car a whisker in front of his. The Jag accelerated forward, but it was all over. The man with the steel-grey eyes braked hard, and the sleek machine slithered to a stop as we joined the column of vehicles heading for the Alexandra Gate.

'Close,' I said, as we drove off.

'No, dear boy, not at all, not at all. It was always

a foregone conclusion.'

'Why do you say that?'

'The Jag was brand new. That's why I chose it.'

'You chose it?'

'Of course! I didn't decide to push in at that particular point by chance – I chose the Jag.'

'Really?'

'Yes, of course.' Bernard smiled. 'Rule number one when gatecrashing a nice orderly queue: always take on the newest, most expensive car you can find. The owner will generally be prepared to go any lengths to avoid an accident which might result in separation from his or her status symbol for days, perhaps weeks, while repairs are effected.'

'If I may say so, Bernard,' I observed, 'the conditions of your car would suggest that several of the owners you've come across managed to overcome their concern about the possible results of a collision.'

'The condition of this vehicle,' Bernard replied, archly, 'is all part of the psychological strategy.'

'You don't say.'

'I most certainly do. Put yourself in that chap in the Jag's place. One look at this car told him something. What was it, Richard?'

'That it's been involved in a number of minor accidents and probably a couple of not so minor ones as well.'

'Exactly, dear boy! It told him that if he didn't stop, his lovely, new, shiny, prestigious emblem of success would stand a good chance of getting seriously bent. It told him that Bernard Thornton does not stop for Jaguars – or anything else for that matter.'

'I see,' I said, pretty certain they weren't the only conclusions the Jaguar driver had come to about my companion.

'And it's not just new, expensive cars the technique works on,' he continued. 'There's one other type of vehicle you can always intimidate using my system.'

'What's that?'

'Taxis.'

'Taxis!' I exclaimed. 'You must be joking. The only experience I've had with a taxi since I've been driving in London was when I was in Knightsbridge heading for Primrose Hill and very nearly ended up in Essex before I shook him off.'

'Well, there you are.'

'Exactly – there I was: in Epping Forest instead of Primrose Hill as a result of trying to take on a London cabby.'

'No, no. What I meant was that was as a result of doing it all wrong. You must *really* take them on – drive straight at them.'

'Are you out of your mind?'

'No, although I am aware that some lesser mortals among Hampson's varied staff regard me as a little eccentric, I can assure you that I am quite sane.'

I raised an eyebrow.

'What you have to remember is that the terms and conditions of a cabby's licence are very strict, and one of those conditions is that no cab shall ply for hire whilst damaged.'

'I didn't know that.'

'No? Well, how many damaged taxis have you seen on the road since you started living in London.'

'None,' I agreed.

'Exactly. That's because no sooner do they have a knock than they're off the road for repairs. The cabby's left twiddling his thumbs, and of course, no cab means no income. That's the key, dear boy, if he bends his cab, he foregoes his income. Drive straight at them – they'll get out of the way.'

Although I was sure Bernard Thornton's approach to driving in London was probably fundamentally sound and based on good psychology, I couldn't help but feel that each of his journeys must have been a little like a suicide mission. As we pulled into Vanbrugh Street I decided I would continue to persevere with my own less aggressive technique.

'Ah, bit of luck,' he said, as we drew up alongside an unoccupied meter.

He put the car into reverse and carefully backed into the bay until, eventually, there came a crunching sound behind us. Without a word, he changed gear and eased the car forward.

'I think you just backed into that car behind us, Bernard,' I said. As I spoke there was another slight grating, grinding noise and the car in front of us bounced up and down. 'You've just hit that one as well,' I said.

'Yes, dear boy, of course,' he replied, in a rather bored tone, as he finally positioned the car in the centre of the bay' 'It's the only way I can be sure I'm properly parked. Why? How do you do it?'

'I don't think I've ever had two worse journeys in my life,' I complained to Charlotte, once I'd attained the safety of our office. 'Trying to get a cab was bad enough, but travelling back with Bernard has put years on me. He's a maniac.'

'Of course he is. But you knew that,' she replied. 'I don't know what possessed you to get into that death-trap of his.'

'The thought of walking back to the office in driving sleet,' I said.

'Ah, well, if you think today's bad, you should hear the weather forecast for tomorrow.'

'Bad?'

'Dreadful – temperatures not above freezing all day and heavy snowfalls in certain areas.'

'Which areas?'

'Guess.'

'The east coast?'

'Yes.'

'Including Colchester?'

'Especially Colchester.'

By the time Sarah Bishop called me back to confirm our arrangements for the following day, she too had been told of the impending blizzard.

'I'd intended to drive down, but I'm not so sure now,' she said. 'I don't really like driving in bad conditions.'

'You're welcome to come down with me if you like,' I offered. 'I'm afraid it'll only be in a Mini, but at least that gives us the advantage of front-wheel drive if the road conditions do get nasty.'

'That's fine. I don't care what it is as long as I don't have to drive it,' she said, adding: 'I hope you're a careful driver, Mr Harton.'

'Miss Bishop,' I replied, 'compared to some I've seen in the last few weeks, I can assure you I am almost pedestrian.'

Chapter 12

Sarah Bishop had sounded bright and efficient over the telephone, but beyond that she was an unknown quantity. It was therefore with a certain sense of curiosity that I drove to the address in Notting Hill which I'd carefully noted down the previous afternoon.

Her flat was in one of the many crescents of town houses long since divided up into flats. I double-parked and got out of the car. It was barely seven o'clock and darkly overcast with a threatening sky which promised to fulfil all the most direful prophecies of the Meteorological Office. To augment the chill temperature, which must have been close to freezing anyway, a stiletto-like east wind stabbed its way down the street. With half-closed eyes I quickly ran over to the front door. Picking out the Entryphone of my passenger-to-be, I pressed the buzzer. After a few moments an inaudible message crackled out at me, then the instrument went dead again. I shuffled back to the car and stood next to it, head down against the wind.

At the sound of the door being opened, I looked up, and through eyes watering with cold I saw a well wrapped-up figure step out into the street. She was carrying a briefcase in one hand and what looked like two slices of toast in the other. A third piece of toast was clamped between her teeth. She turned to close the door behind her, hesitated and finally put down her briefcase.

'Would you like a hand?' I asked, stepping forward.

She took a bite out of the piece of toast she had been holding in her mouth, and nodded enthusiastically.

'Yes, please,' she said. 'Could you take my briefcase?'

'Of course,' I replied, picking it up.

'And have a slice of toast,' she went on. 'I've made more than I want.'

'Well, if you're sure . . .'

'Certain – here you are,' she said, pressing a sticky slice of marmalade toast into my hand. 'I hope you like Mrs Cooper's Old English – if I don't get my morning fix I just keel over. Can we stop for some coffee on the way? I didn't have a chance to make any. Will there be time?'

'I should think so.'

'Good – well, let's go,' she said, going round to the passenger door.

'Okay. Do you want your briefcase or shall I put it in the back?'

'I'd better have it, then we can go over the valuation on the way. Frankly, I don't know much about it. It's been dropped on my desk because the person handling it has been away, and the beneficiary's suddenly screaming for action – hence the rush.'

'Fine.' I got into the car, leant across and opened the passenger door.

A moment later we were on our way.

Despite being dressed up like a Michelin Man, my companion was certainly very attractive. Her hair was honey-blonde and her eyes, a piercing, vivid blue, were set off by little laugh lines. Suddenly, the prospect of getting cut off by heavy snow in darkest Essex didn't seem too bad at all.

'I usually deal with commercial business,' she said, as she leafed through the file, 'so this is all new to me. I suppose you spend your whole working life doing this sort of thing.'

'Quite a lot of it.'

166

'It must be interesting.'

'Sometimes, yes, but like any job there's a lot of repetitive routine.'

'I suppose so,' she went on, still thumbing through the file, 'but you must get to meet lots of different people.'

'Oh, yes, although it must be said that they've changed rather a lot since I started in the business ten years ago.'

'In what way?' she asked, looking up from her now untidy pile of papers.

'Well, when I first worked in Sussex, people would bring things along to our auction galleries, and their first question would be "What is it?" The second question would be "Can you sell it?"'

'What do they say now?'

'Now, all they ask is "What's it worth?" And that's usually just after they've told *me* what it is.'

'Oh, dear, you sound rather disillusioned.'

'No, not really,' I said. 'It's just a pity that everybody thinks more about what a thing's worth than about whether it's nice or not.'

She smiled. 'But surely it's you auctioneers who've encouraged us all to believe there's a fortune lurking in our attics?'

'Yes, you're right, of course. It's as much our fault as anybody's – still a pity, though.'

'Ah, well, you can't expect to have your cake and eat it. Anyway, if you're used to dealing with unpleasant, penny-pinching, misanthropes, you'll feel perfectly at home with our client this morning.'

I grinned at her. 'I begin to suspect you don't like him.'

'Did I say that?'

'No, I just seemed to get the impression . . .'

'Good Lord, no. There's nothing wrong with Jonathan Pellman – especially if you like misogynists.'

'I think we'd better stop for that coffee soon,' I said. 'I think your caffeine level's becoming dangerously low.'

'You could be right,' she replied.

Over coffee from a wayside van, Sarah Bishop gave me the background to the valuation. Not that there was much to tell. The deceased was an old lady who, since the death of her husband many years earlier, had lived in the house we were going to, attended only by an elderly housekeeper. Although the property was going to be put on the market, it was unlikely that any of the contents would be sold since the son – my companion's favourite client – had said he intended to keep everything. As to just where he intended to put it all, Sarah Bishop neither knew nor cared. There was little silver, no jewellery and only a few pictures. We would have the octogenarian housekeeper to look after our needs, and the son would be coming along to join us at some stage during the latter part of the morning.

'I take it Mr Pellman isn't an easy man to deal with,' I said, when she had completed her very concise summary of affairs.

'Now, whatever makes you say that, Mr Harton?'

'Well, it could be that, just a few moments ago, you described him as unpleasant, penny-pinching . . .'

'No, no. You must have heard wrongly. I'm never rude about my clients – even if they are slobs.'

'I was obviously mistaken,' I said, gravely.

'Spoken like a man who doesn't want this to be his first and last job with MacGregor Roche. Anyway, you may like Mr Pellman. He'll probably be nice as pie to you. The way men react to one another is different to the way they react to women.'

'Oh, I don't think so.'

'Oh, I know so,' she smiled.

'I'm really not sure I agree . . .'

'Of course you don't – you're a man.'

'That's not got anything to do with it . . .'

'It's got everything to do with it,' she insisted, still smiling. 'You're a man so you don't notice the difference in behaviour of other men to women because you behave differently yourself.'

'I don't!'

'Of course you do,' she went on, obviously enjoying herself. 'Let's take an easy example – tell me, what were your first thoughts when we met this morning?'

'Why has that solicitor got a slice of toast in her mouth.'

'And after that?' she smiled indulgently.

'Well, I suppose . . . I . . . er . . .'

'Exactly, and I'm sure you'll admit that whatever it was, it wasn't the same thought you would have had had I been a man.'

'You can say that again,' I muttered as I turned my head to look out of my window.

'Sorry?'

'Yes, I do admit that,' I said.

It was very early in the morning for any sort of argument on feminism, and it was already evident I was on a hiding to nothing. Sarah Bishop had trod that road before.

The late Mrs Pellman's home turned out to be a nice old rectory dating from about 1810. The main house was almost square with a single storey wing which looked to be a Victorian addition. A blue car covered in a recent sprinkling of snow already stood in the driveway. I drove up next to it and parked.

'Your client?' I asked, looking across at the motor.

'I wouldn't have thought so. I can't imagine that Jonathan Pellman has a reputation for being early, but, on the other hand, I don't know who else it could be.'

We gathered our things together, pulled up our collars, and scuttled over to the front door where Sarah pressed urgently on the old polished brass bell.

The door was opened after some time by a robust,

grey-haired woman. Her expression suggested she was not expecting callers.

'Yes?' she said.

'Mrs Healey?' my companion asked doubtfully.

'No, I'm afraid not, my dear,' the woman said.

'Well, I wonder if I might see her. She is expecting us – I'm Sarah Bishop from MacGregor Roche, and this is Richard Harton from Hampson's.'

It was obvious from the woman's face that the names meant nothing to her. 'It's rather difficult at the moment, my dear,' she said. 'You see, Mrs Healey's ill.'

'Not seriously, I hope.'

'I'm rather afraid it is serious, yes. Very serious, in fact. The doctor's with her now.'

This did not sound promising. I had intended to get the valuation over and done with, then back on the road in case the weather really closed in.

'Perhaps I could have a word with the doctor,' Sarah Bishop suggested. 'You see, I'm from the solicitors handling Mrs Pellman's estate.'

'Oh, I see,' the woman said, 'I'm sorry. I didn't realise. I'll just go and see if the doctor can come and have a word.'

We were left standing just inside the front door as she went to find the GP. She didn't climb the stairs in front of us, but instead went through a green baize-covered doorway in the far corner of the hall.

'I wonder what's wrong with Mrs Healey,' Sarah said.

'Pneumonia I would think. The temperature in this place is nothing short of arctic.'

'Don't joke about it – she's very old.'

'I can assure you, Miss Bishop, I am not joking.'

She looked at me and grinned. 'You can call me Sarah, if I can call you . . . ' She stopped in mid-sentence as the green baize door opened, admitting a man in his thirties. He was dressed in a tweed sports jacket and corduroy trousers and his stethoscope still hung about his neck.

He crossed the hall towards us.

'Hello, I'm Hugh Carter – Mrs Healey's doctor,' he said, addressing me. 'I understand you're from the family solicitors.'

'Actually, I'm Richard Harton of Hampson's the auctioneers,' I said. 'It's Miss Bishop here who's with the solicitors.'

'I'm sorry,' he said, turning to her, 'I just assumed . . .'

'Don't worry about it,' she said, 'I'm used to it. I understand that Mrs Healey's unwell.'

'I'm afraid, Miss Bishop, that Mrs Healey is dying.'

'Dying!'

'I'm afraid so.'

'What's actually the matter with her?' I asked.

'Quite honestly, the poor old thing's just plain worn out, although the immediate problem is pneumonia. I understand it set in yesterday but I wasn't called out until early this morning. All I can do, to be frank, is keep her as comfortable as possible.'

'But, shouldn't she be in hospital?' Sarah asked.

'Probably, but there are a few obstacles to arranging that at the moment.'

'What?' I enquired.

'Firstly, in her lucid moments, the old lady keeps telling me she's ready to die and begs me to let her do it here. Secondly, I can't get her a bed at any of the local hospitals. Thirdly, we are in the middle of an ambulance dispute – they're not coming out for anything.'

'Oh, of course,' I said. 'I'd forgotten about that.'

'Well, it's a real problem,' Dr Carter continued. 'So the only thing I can do now is to try to ensure she's not left alone for too long.'

'Left alone?' Sarah frowned. 'Surely she can't be left alone at all, can she?'

'I certainly agree she shouldn't be,' the doctor replied, 'but the problem is human resources. I'll call back later

171

but obviously I can't stay here all the time. I'm trying to arrange some cover with the district nurse, and Mrs Tarrant, the lady who let you in, is going to stay here until this evening.'

'Is she a relative?' I asked.

'No, just a neighbour – and a jolly good one at that. She was the one who found Mrs Healey and called me this morning. She's been tremendous.'

'Mr Pellman's due to meet us here later this morning,' Sarah said. 'Perhaps he'll be able to help in some way.'

'Well, it would be nice if he showed some interest,' Dr Carter said, coldly. 'After all, the old lady worked for his mother for donkey's years. Anyway, I must go. I'll pop back at lunchtime to see how things are.'

'The good doctor seems to share your opinion of your client,' I said, after the GP had gone.

'Yes, I got that impression too. I wasn't sure whether he'd met him or not, but if he hasn't it would seem Mr Pellman's reputation has preceded him.'

'Well, whichever it is, I think it's amazing.'

'What?'

'Oh, the fact that the doctor agrees with you even though he's a man.'

'Ah! Very clever! But, on the other hand, perhaps you'll recall that he made the immediate assumption that you, the man, were the solicitor.'

'Miss Bishop – I think you're just a bad loser.'

'Mr Harton – I wouldn't know. I can't remember when I last lost.'

I smiled. 'Thirty all?'

'I'd go along with that,' she grinned.

'Right,' I said, 'I must get on with this valuation if we're ever going to get back to London tonight.'

'Can I do anything to help?'

'It would certainly speed things up if you could take notes for me.'

'Fine. I'll just be twiddling my thumbs until Pellman

arrives, otherwise.'

I took a notebook from my briefcase and handed it to her. 'By the way, I agree,' I said, 'I think we should make it Richard and Sarah.'

'Done,' she replied.

The house itself turned out to be as nice inside as it appeared outside. The rooms were well proportioned, light and airy. I suppose, under the right conditions, they might also have been quite cosy; but they merited no such adjective that day.

'You were right,' Sarah said, as we quickly made our way round the ground floor, 'this place is absolutely freezing.'

'Yes, I should think your friend, Mr Pellman, must have been hovering with his finger on the heating switch at the exact moment his mother shuffled off the mortal coil.'

'Oh, I'm not sure he'd wait that long.'

My provisional look at the contents didn't take long. Within fifteen minutes I had a good picture of what the job was all about, with the exception that is, of what might lie behind the green baize door.

'I don't want to disturb what's going on in there until I have to,' I said, 'so we'll get the main contents done with first.'

'How long do you think it will take?' Sarah asked.

'This part of it – no more than a couple of hours I would think.'

'Okay. Incidentally, what do you think of it? Is there anything any good here? I don't know the first thing about antiques.'

'There are some nice pieces here,' I replied. 'Mind you, not so long ago, there were quite a few more.'

She looked puzzled. 'What do you mean?'

'I mean someone has been busy redistributing a little wealth.'

'What? Are you saying the place has been burgled?'

173

'No, no. Burglars don't half-inch the Bechstein then rearrange the occasional tables so you don't notice it's missing.'

'Is that what's happened?' she asked, still looking confused.

'Yes, every room has lost an item or two, and I wouldn't mind betting that some of the furniture here now has been substituted for better pieces.'

'Are you sure?'

'Yes,' I replied. 'Have another look at the drawing room. I'll show you what I mean.'

The drawing room was probably the nicest room in the house. Running the entire length of the rectory, it faced south and had big windows on three sides. One wall boasted a large fireplace with an elegant Louis XV marble surround which was unquestionably the focal point of the room.

'Now,' I said, 'have a look round and tell me what's wrong.'

She wandered across the room, looking around her as she went. Then she stopped, bent down, and examined the carpet.

'Something's been moved from here,' she said.

'Spot on. Not only has it been moved from there, it's been moved from the house – it's gone completely.'

'How do you know whatever it is isn't in the house-keeper's wing, for safekeeping, say?'

'I don't, but considering what it was I doubt that the unfortunate Mrs Healey shipped it through there on her own. And, anyway, it's not the type of thing one tends to hide away for safekeeping.'

'Why? What was it . . . hold on . . . it was a piano!'

'Right again,' I said, walking over to where she stood. 'Just the three deep marks in the carpet. From the size of it it must have been a baby grand.'

'Is there anything else missing from this room?' she asked.

'At least two chairs, a small table and a large picture.'

'A picture?'

'Yes, almost certainly an oil painting. It used to hang over the fireplace where that mirror's hanging now.'

'How can you be so sure? The wall isn't marked or anything?'

'No, by the look of it the room was redecorated not very long ago. But, I'll bet you a pound to a penny that the late Mrs Pellman was not responsible for putting that mirror there.'

'Oh, come on,' she said. 'How can you be so sure?'

'Look, even allowing for the missing pieces, this house has been furnished with some taste – wouldn't you agree?' I said.

'Yes.'

'And that fireplace is the focal point of this room?'

'Yes.'

'And it's a Louis XV surround worth several thousand pounds?'

'If you say so.'

'And that mirror is a rather nasty modern reproduction?'

'Who am I to argue with an expert?'

'So putting all those points together, do you really believe that your late client, Mrs Pellman – that's the cultivated, tasteful and refined Mrs Pellman – would really have looked at that piece of junk over the mantelpiece and thought it was just the thing for there?'

'Mmmm,' she said, 'I begin to see what you mean.'

'And,' I went on, 'I'm sure you don't need three guesses as to the villain of the piece.'

'No, I suppose it's got to be my favourite beneficiary minimising his tax liability. What a toad! I know it happens all the time, but he has gone in for it on a grand scale.'

'I know, but there's nothing we can do about it.'

'No,' she replied, shaking her head, 'but it does

rankle. There he was the other day complaining that we hadn't had the valuation done, whereas if we'd turned up a couple of days ago we would probably have caught him red-handed with the piano on the back of his bike.'

I nodded. 'Almost certainly. Never mind, let's get started on what he's left for us.'

'Yes,' she said, perching on the arm of a chair, pen and notebook at the ready.

'Drawing Room,' I began. 'Item One – A Queen Anne walnut side chair, the seat covered in floral tapestry panel, raised on cabriole legs . . .'

A little over two hours later the valuation of the main house contents was complete. Sarah and I stood in the hallway by the green baize door. It was time to have a look at the kitchen and domestic quarters.

'You stay here if you want to,' I said. 'I don't expect this will take me very long.'

'No, it's all right, I . . . ' She was interrupted by the telephone on the hall table. 'I suppose I'd better answer that,' she said.

As she went over to answer the phone, I quietly opened the baize-covered door and slipped into another world.

Whereas the main house had been modernised, and was well maintained and decorated, the passageway in which I found myself was dark and Victorian. I stood just inside the door and listened. The only sound I could hear was the muffled voice of Sarah as she spoke on the telephone. I walked quietly down the passage and knocked gently on the first door I came to. There was no response. I opened the door and stuck my head round it. It was a sitting room, sparsely furnished and with a particularly gloomy outlook over a small, enclosed yard. The next room looked to be a bedroom, although the bed had been removed. Then came a primitive bathroom and some sort of scullery or pantry. After that only one door remained, closed and silent, at the far end of the passage. I was just about to knock when I heard the baize door open behind me. It was Sarah and she didn't look happy.

'Would you believe it . . . ?' she started.

I held my finger up to my lips to remind her that we had somebody dying nearby.

'Would you believe it?' she whispered.

'Probably – what?'

'Pellman isn't coming after all. That was him on the telephone . . .'

Again I held a finger to my lips as her voice began to rise.

'That was him on the telephone,' she repeated, reverting to a whisper. 'He called to say he has a bit of a cold and doesn't want to make it worse by coming here to this horribly cold house.'

'Is that what he said?' I asked.

'Word for word.'

'Did you explain about Mrs Healey?'

'Yes, I told him exactly what the position is.'

'What did he say?'

'Oh, dear!'

'That was it, was it?'

'No. He also said it was a shame, and when I told him that the old lady might be left on her own tonight he said he was sure it would all sort itself out. What a slob! The only way . . .'

Once again I held up a warning finger.

' . . . the only way it could all sort itself out,' she hissed, 'would be if poor Mrs Healey suddenly picked up her bed and walked.'

'So he's not going to do anything.'

'Absolutely nothing,' she fumed.

'Well, let's just hope the doctor's been able to arrange something with the district nurse,' I said.

'Yes,' she replied. 'By the way, where is Mrs Healey?'

'In there, I assume.' I pointed to the door behind me

in the passage. 'Her bedroom appears to be just along there on the right, but the bed's been moved out.'

'You haven't seen her yet, then?'

'No, I was just going in when you arrived.'

'Okay, ready when you are.'

I turned and tapped gently on the door in question. A few moments later it was opened by Mrs Tarrant.

'Hello,' she said.

'Hello, Mrs Tarrant. We've finished the rest of the valuation and I really need to have a quick look around in here now. Is it possible? I don't want to disturb Mrs Healey.'

'Oh, you won't disturb her,' she said. 'Dr Carter's given her some sort of sedative. She was very distressed, the poor dear, but she's just sleeping peacefully now. You come on in and do whatever you have to.'

Followed by Sarah, I stepped into one of the most antiquated kitchens I'd ever seen.

It was a large stone-flagged room. The high ceiling was set with a skylight, but that was so heavily coated in grime it barely lit the room at all. The only other natural illumination came from a small window above an old, shallow earthenware sink. The furniture was basic. There was a big, scrubbed pine table and an assortment of chairs. On one wall was a painted pine dresser littered with an assortment of crockery. On the opposite wall, an Aga (apparently the only item to have been installed in the last fifty years) was acting as the only heat source in the entire house.

Next to the Aga, in an old brass-and-iron bedstead, lay the late Mrs Pellman's housekeeper. Propped up on a pile of pillows and framed by her long pure-white hair, the grey, toothless face with its white lips and hollowed cheeks looked totally drained of life. It was only the dreadful noise of her breathing that confirmed she was still clinging to this life rather than having already slipped unnoticed into the next. I stood frozen for a moment, listening. There was a long, drawn-out rattling wheeze as she breathed in, then a silence, then another rasping rattle as she expelled the air again. It was exhausting just to listen to. The strain involved seemed more than the tiny worn-out body could possibly bear. Another long silence followed, then the whole laboured process began again.

'We brought her in here because it's the only warm room in the house,' Mrs Tarrant explained.

'However did you move the bed?' I asked. 'It must have been a major job.'

'My husband, Tom, came round and between him, Doctor Carter and me, we managed it.'

'Were you the one who found her?' I asked.

'Yes. I'd been keeping an eye on her for some time now. I suppose, really, she's been going downhill fast since Mrs Pellman died, but this was very sudden. I just looked across this morning and saw there were no lights on – she was always up by six – so Tom and I came over and found her like this. I think she's just given up – that's the truth of it.'

'These conditions can't have helped her much,' I said, looking around the dismal room.

'No, it's awful isn't it. But then it's as much her fault as anybody else's you know. If old Mrs Pellman ever did offer to spend any money on the place, then Maud here wouldn't have any of it. She'd just got too old, too stuck in her ways. She couldn't change, you see.'

I turned to look at Sarah. She was staring, fixedly, at the bed and its occupant.

'There are only a few things I need to note down in here,' I said.

She started as though she'd been brought out of a trance. 'What?' she said. 'I'm sorry, I didn't catch what you said.'

'I said, there are only a few things to note down in here, then I'll be finished.'

179

'Oh, yes, fine,' she said, her eyes returning to Mrs Healey.

I quickly checked through the cupboards and drawers and recorded everything worthy of mention. Finally, I jotted down a figure to cover all the remaining bits, then I closed my notebook and replaced my pen in my pocket.

'I understand there's a problem about anybody being free to sit with Mrs Healey tonight,' I said to Mrs Tarrant, as I washed my hands at the old sink.

'Yes, Tom's on night shift and I've promised to look after my eldest daughter's boy, otherwise we would have sat with her. As it is, I just don't see what we can do.' She looked over to the bed. 'It would be awful for her to be left, though,' she said, dropping her voice to a whisper. 'I really don't think she's going to get through the night.'

'She certainly seems very weak,' I agreed.

Mrs Tarrant nodded.

'The doctor's due back soon, isn't he?' I asked.

'Yes, he said he'd come back at lunchtime.'

'Okay, I think that rather than going straight back to London, Miss Bishop and I will grab a bite to eat at the local pub and then pop back to see if he's had any luck with arranging for the district nurse to help.'

'All right,' Mrs Tarrant replied, 'I'll see you later.'

Sarah and I made our way along the dark passageway in silence. As soon as we were back in the hall I turned to her.

'That old lady cannot be left alone tonight,' I said.

'I know,' she said. 'If the district nurse can't get here I'll stay with her.'

'What?'

'I'll stay with her.'

'You won't have to,' I said.

'Why?'

'Because I've already made up my mind that I'm going to stay.'

'You?'

180

'Yes.'

'But that's ridiculous – it's got nothing to do with you.'

'It's got as much to do with me as it has with you.'

'No it hasn't, Richard. I'm representing the solicitors in charge of Mrs Pellman's estate . . .'

'Look, I'm not going to stand around here arguing about it,' I said. 'If you want to discuss it we can do it at the pub.'

'There's nothing to discuss . . .'

After a quarter of an hour in front of the fire in the local pub a sense of feeling had returned to my hands and feet, as had a sense of proportion to our argument.

'I don't think it matters one bit that you're with MacGregor Roche and Partners or that I'm with Hampson's,' I said. 'All that really matters is that that old lady doesn't die alone tonight.'

'I know,' Sarah said, stirring the soup around in the bowl in front of her, 'but I do feel it's my responsibility.'

'Mrs Healey does not form part of Mrs Pellman's estate,' I pointed out. 'She's just a human being like us. She's as much my responsibility as yours or Mrs Tarrant's or anybody else's.'

Sarah sighed and put down her spoon. 'I still feel it's up to me – I can't help it.'

'Why don't we toss for it?' I suggested.

'What!'

'Why don't we toss for it?'

'We can't do that.'

'Of course we can,' I said, taking a ten pence piece from my pocket. 'We'll toss for it. The loser stays with Mrs Healey, the winner goes back to London. No further discussion, no right of appeal. Okay?'

'Oh, well, all right,' she said, reluctantly. 'I suppose it's as good a way to decide as any – go on.'

I spun the coin, caught it, and slapped it down on the back of my hand. 'Call,' I said.

'Tails.'

181

'Tails it is,' I confirmed.

Sarah leant over the table and looked at the coin. 'Best of three,' she suggested.

'No,' I said, firmly, 'that's it – I'm the one who will stay if the doctor hasn't managed to arrange anything.'

'Well, I'm still not sure . . .'

'Well, I am, so all we have to decide now is whether you would like to take my car back to London or whether you'd prefer me to run you to the nearest station.'

'I'd rather not drive in this weather,' she replied.

'That's fine. We'll find out about trains when we get back to the house,' I said. 'Talking of which – I'm ready when you are.'

A fresh fall of dry, powdery snow was being whipped into miniature whirlwinds in front of the rectory when we turned back into the driveway. Once again, Dr Carter's car stood outside the front door, and as before it was Mrs Tarrant who let us in.'

'How are things?' I asked.

'Oh, no change really, my dear,' she replied. 'She's just sinking, slowly but steadily. Dr Carter's very good. He's making it easy for her.'

'Any luck with the district nurse?' Sarah asked.

'No, I'm afraid not.'

'Never mind,' I said, 'Miss Bishop and I have talked it over and I'm perfectly prepared to stay with Mrs Healey tonight if nobody else can sit with her.'

'Oh, what a kind thought.'

'That's all right,' I said. 'I'll just have to check on train times and drop Miss Bishop at the station . . .'

'No, no, you don't have to worry, my dear,' Mrs Tarrant interrupted.

'Sorry?'

'You don't have to worry yourself about it. Maud won't be on her own. It's all right.'

'Who's going to be with her?' Sarah asked.

182

'Me,' Mrs Tarrant said. 'Tom telephoned – couldn't have been more than five minutes after you went for lunch – to say that he'd swapped his night shift with one of his mates. So, I got onto my daughter and rearranged things with her as well.'

'Well, that's good,' I said.

'Yes, my dear. Tom and I'll sit with Maud. She won't be on her own. Don't you worry.'

The windscreen wipers slapped to and fro noisily as we drove through the wet, slushy snow in the Mile End Road. Sarah stirred for almost the first time since leaving the rectory.

'Good sleep?' I asked.

'Yes – goodness, how rude of me,' she replied. 'You should have woken me up.'

'Why? You must have needed it.'

She giggled. 'You sound like my mother.'

'Well, thank you very much!' I replied.

As it happened, I had been quite grateful for the silent journey back to London. It had given me time to think. I had only known Sarah Bishop for a day, but there was no doubt that she had made an impression. She was bright, intelligent and good-looking. She was also the first person to whom I had felt seriously attracted since Antonia and I had gone our separate ways, and that was quite something.

It was almost seven months since we had split up, and in that time I had swapped the quiet rural life for the bright lights of London, and a steady no-risk job for what promised to be death or glory at Hampson's. Unfortunately, the one thing that hadn't changed was how I felt about Antonia: I was still in love with her. That was all very well of course, but I couldn't go on moping my life away for ever. Perhaps now was the time to snap out of it. I decided I would ask Sarah out to dinner.

But what if she said no? Why should I assume she

wasn't already heavily involved with somebody, after all she was *very* attractive. Perhaps she was living with someone – I didn't know who else might share her flat. The last thing I wanted was to be politely told to go and boil my head. But that was just cowardice, wasn't it? Surely I was made of sterner stuff than that, wasn't I? On the other hand, perhaps it would be wiser to wait. I could find out more about her; ask her out next time we met, perhaps. No, that was no good. I probably wouldn't have any reason to speak to her again about this job, and she wouldn't be handling another – she would go straight back to her commercial work. No, it was now or never. I took a deep breath . . .

'Do you think Mrs Healey will live through the night?' she asked, suddenly.

'I . . . what? . . . sorry? . . .'

She repeated her question.

'I don't think it's very likely,' I said, regaining a little composure.

'No, that's what I thought,' she replied, her head half turned away from me as she gazed out of her window. 'I am glad it's not me sitting with the poor old lady,' she added.

'Me too. I would have done it, but I can't say I was looking forward to it.'

'Never mind,' she said, looking from the street to me, 'at least you were prepared to help – unlike the dreadful Mr Pellman.'

She turned away again and we drove on, in silence once more, towards the prestigious City offices of MacGregor Roche; my opportunity melting away with each minute that passed.

'I'll get the valuation typed up tomorrow,' I said, as we pulled up outside the marble-clad building that was both destination and deadline.

'Fine,' Sarah replied, putting on her scarf and pulling up her collar.

'Just let me know if there are any problems,' I went on, still trying to buy time.

'Will do,' she confirmed, gathering up her briefcase and opening the car door.

'Er . . . Sarah . . .'

'Yes, Richard.'

'I was wondering if . . .'

'Yes, Richard?'

Oh, hell! She could only tell me to get lost once. 'I was wondering if you would like to have a bite to eat one evening.' The words tumbled out.

'Yes, Richard, I would,' she said. Then she smiled. 'I thought you were never going to ask.'

'You're looking very smug,' Charlotte observed when I arrived back at Hampson's. 'It must have been a good valuation.'

'It was certainly unusual.'

'And Miss Bishop?'

'What about her?'

'I just wondered what she was like.'

'Oh, all right I suppose.'

'Just all right?'

'Yes. Why?'

'Oh, I just thought she might be something a little special.'

'Why should you think that?'

'I don't know.' She looked thoughtful for a moment, then seemed to decide on something. 'Perhaps it's because she's the only solicitor you've made a pass at . . .'

'What?'

'. . . since you've been at Hampson's, anyway. Of course, I can't speak for what you used to get up to in Sussex.'

'What do you . . . how do you . . .'

'It's all right, Richard,' Charlotte beamed, 'I know everything . . . you don't have to lie . . .'

'Charlotte!'

'Yes, Richard,' she said, fluttering her eyelids and smiling sweetly.

'What are you talking about?'

'She's just telephoned, my little Lothario.'

'Oh.'

'Oh, indeed,' she continued, picking up a scrap of paper and scrutinising it, 'and here is the message she left for you. Which would you like first – the bad news or the not-quite-so-bad news?'

I sat down at my desk and glared at Charlotte. 'The bad news, and without frills, please.'

'Whatever you say, Boss. The bad news is . . . are you ready for this?'

'Charlotte!'

'Sorry, sorry . . . the bad news is that Miss Bishop can't make it for dinner at eight o'clock on Friday after all.'

My heart sank. 'Oh, damn it!'

'However, the not-quite-so-bad news is that I am available on that evening.'

'Ho, ho – very funny.'

'If I may say so, Richard, that is not a very flattering response to an offer for which several love-sick males I know would give their eye-teeth and considerable numbers of luncheon vouchers.'

'Charlotte!'

'No, now, don't get snappy – I was only joking. The real not-quite-so-bad news is that she'll be ready by eight-thirty. It's just that she had a meeting put in her diary while she was out today, and it might run on a bit.'

'So dinner's still on.'

'Yes, you shall go to the ball, Cinderella,' she said. 'Now, before you fill me in on what's so marvellous about Sarah Bishop, there's one other important message.'

'What's that?'

'Patrick Faulkner has – and I quote – "picked up a big one".'

186

'Oh, dear. Has he seen his GP about it?'

'Good to see the old sense of humour's returned,' Charlotte observed. 'Anyway, Fatty Faulkner says it's a good probate valuation near Godalming. I think everything's going to be sold, and he wants you to go down there with him tomorrow to do the valuation.'

'I haven't got anything else on, have I?' I asked.

'No, I checked your diary: it's all clear. I said you'd be there by eight o'clock.'

'Fine. Anything else?'

'Yes, there was one other little thing.'

'What's that?'

'Well, going back to my telephone conversation with your new playmate, Sarah . . .'

'Yes,' I said, very warily.

'Well, just before she rang off, she asked me a question.'

'What was it?'

'I'm not sure I should tell you.'

'Charlotte!'

'All right, all right. She asked me if you are a skier.'

'A skier?'

'Yes, odd isn't it? Just where are you thinking of taking her for dinner on Friday – St Moritz or Gstaad?'

Chapter 13

The Lodge, at Blackwood near Godalming was an adventure in Victorian architectural excess. Its only concession to the locality was that it was built of rough-hewn stone from a nearby quarry, otherwise it was as out of keeping with its surroundings as would have been a hacienda in Frimley High Street.

It was an asymmetrical muddle of towers, turrets, lancet windows and bogus armorial stained glass. But, whereas its source of inspiration seemed to bubble from the twin fountainheads of Balmoral and Bavaria, its scale had clearly been dictated by the somewhat limited disposable income appropriate to a modestly successful nineteenth century, Surrey, professional man. It must have been dreadfully frustrating for both owner and architect. They had wanted to build a castle, but finances had limited them to a house – albeit a large one. As a result, the inevitable conflicts which ensued were gloriously documented in every feature of the eventual compromise: the whole structure was one big gory battlefield.

'Pretty gruesome isn't it?' Patrick Faulkner commented, as he parked his car on the weed-strewn cobbles outside what must once have been the coach house and stable block.

'Black Forest Grampian?' I suggested.

'More like Black Forest Gateau. But wait till you see the inside.'

My journey to Blackwood that morning had been an interesting one. The slight contact I'd had until then with Patrick Faulkner had left me with the distinct impression that he was not altogether trustworthy. There was certainly a superficial charm about the man, but I suspected his driving force was nothing deeper than narrow self-interest. Although I learnt no great secrets during the trip, I did come away with the feeling that there was more to him than the brash bonhomie he projected. He volunteered that he was divorced and poor – directly attributing the latter to the former – and he also admitted to being fifty. That came as a surprise since, despite the excess weight he carried, he still looked younger. He had three grown-up children who he rarely saw, and a passion for jazz which he seldom indulged. He made a point of the fact that, along with Charles Morrison-Whyte, he had been with Hampson's before Bob Derby had arrived on the scene. He then went on to heap fulsome praise on the Chairman's head for the development of the company, concluding with the words: 'but, as Charles always says, that's Bob's forte – sales and marketing.' This final assessment of Robert Derby's talents was delivered in the sort of tone one might use for explaining that somebody has an unspecified but probably terminal social disease. It was a deft piece of work. I was left in no doubt as to his true opinion of the Chairman and yet he'd not uttered a single critical word about him. Patrick Faulkner was obviously one of life's great survivors.

Although not a complete wilderness, the garden of the lodge was generally unkempt. We navigated the cracked stone path with great care since the previous afternoon's sleet and rain had frozen hard overnight making parts of it lethal. Once in the porch, Patrick tugged on the old bell-pull.

'The elderly housekeeper's still coming in daily although she's not living here any more,' he explained.

'As long as she's still living,' I said.

'What? Oh, of course – your experience yesterday. Yes, a nasty business. Never mind, I understand Mrs . . . ' he thumbed through his notes, ' . . . Mrs Cook's hail and hearty, although apparently a bit wobbly on her pins.'

At that moment, a couple of rumbling crashes issued from the other side of the nail-studded oak door, as heavy, metal bolts were drawn back. The old lock rattled and grated, then, very slowly, the door was opened.

Mrs Cook was indeed hail and hearty, although she stood no higher than five foot three or four and was perfectly cylindrical. Well wrapped up against the cold, her little pink face just peeped out from below a purple hat which was secured in place by a woollen scarf.

'Good morning,' she said, smiling happily at us.

'Good morning,' Patrick replied. 'You must be Mrs Cook. I'm Patrick Faulkner of Hampson's and this is my colleague, Richard Harton.'

'I'm Mrs Cook,' the lady announced. 'You must be from the auctioneers.'

Patrick smiled indulgently and, raising his voice to a bellow, repeated his previous introduction.

'Oh, yes,' Mrs Cook said, nodding vaguely and still beaming.

'Deaf as a post,' Patrick observed, in a swift aside to me. 'WE'LL COME IN THEN, SHALL WE,' he roared to the still smiling lady.

'You'd better come in,' she said, shuffling back out of the way.

'This could take longer than I'd anticipated,' my companion muttered, as we stepped inside.

We found ourselves in an oak-panelled, miniature baronial hall. An absurdly ornate series of mantel shelves towered above the huge fireplace, while the remaining wall-space dripped with weapons and slightly

190

moth-eaten, leering trophy heads. One, a particularly resentful-looking red deer stag with a crumbling ear, seemed to have doubled over the years as some sort of eccentric hatstand, with each point of its antlers boasting a different style of headgear. There was everything there from a fez to an old German helmet.

'According to the solicitor,' Patrick explained, as we both studied the display, 'the late incumbent, Wilfred Harris Carr Esquire, was what we English tend to describe as a colourful character.'

'I take it you mean he was a complete lunatic.'

'Yes, old boy,' he drawled, 'I would think that's about the size of it – too much inbreeding I expect.'

Insulated in her own little silent world, Mrs Cook stood patiently observing us as we observed the surroundings. I got the impression that she saw us as a far greater curiosity than anything The Lodge might contain.

'Have you been here before?' I asked my companion.

'No, but it's been so vividly described to me by the solicitor I feel I've known it for years.' He turned to the still smiling housekeeper: 'Mrs Cook, don't feel you have to hang around just for us. We can get along perfectly well on our own – as long as everywhere's unlocked.'

The beaming Mrs Cook nodded enthusiastically and firmly stood her ground.

'Oh, God,' Patrick muttered, 'here we go again – YOU CARRY ON WITH ANYTHING YOU HAVE TO DO,' he bawled, reddening a little in the face. 'WE'LL BE JUST FINE.'

'Yes,' Mrs Cook responded, 'it's a bit mucky now, but then you can't keep a place like this clean unless you're at it all the time.'

Faulkner glanced at me and raised his eyebrows. 'QUITE!' he agreed, smiling inanely.

'Well, if there's nothing else you want me for at the

moment,' Mrs Cook went on, 'I'll just pop down to the shops.'

'THAT'S FINE,' I shouted.

'ABSOLUTELY!' added my colleague.

Mrs Cook duly gathered herself up, took aim at the still open front door and, by cleverly exploiting a strange series of rocking movements, generated an erratic form of forward propulsion. By the time she reached the doorway she was rolling rythmically along like one of those heavy-bottomed wobbly toys which always return to upright no matter how hard you knock them over. The similarity was enhanced by Mrs Cook's legs: they were so bowed they formed a very nearly perfect 'O'.

'I doubt we'll see a better pair of cabrioles all day,' Patrick observed, after some serious critical consideration.

I nodded in agreement, then a thought struck me: 'She'll never make it down the path,' I said, 'not with all that ice on it.'

'You have a point, dear boy,' he agreed. 'If her brakes lock-up on that lot the herbaceous border's history.'

I hurried after Mrs Cook, catching up with her just as she was about to take her first step on the treacherous stones.

'Let me help you,' I said, taking her gently by the elbow. 'The path's terribly slippery this morning.'

She gave me another of those blank uncomprehending smiles.

'IT'S VERY SLIPPERY,' I shouted. 'I'LL HELP YOU.'

'You be careful, Mr Hampson,' she said, looking serious for a moment, 'this path's always very slippery after a frost.'

'YES, I'LL GIVE YOU A HAND. HOLD ON TO . . .'

It all happened so quickly. One moment I was bawling cautions and advice to Mrs Cook, and the next she was bending over me asking if I was all right.

'You did go down hard, Mr Hampson,' she tutted. 'Are you sure you're not hurt?'

'No . . . no . . . I'm just . . . a bit . . . winded . . .' I gasped. Not that it was worth the effort, since almost certainly Mrs Cook didn't hear a word.

'That's what I was telling you,' she went on, 'this old path gets awful slippery. You have to be really careful on it.'

'Are you all right, old boy?' Patrick Faulkner called, from the safety of the porch.

'Yes . . . OUCH!'

'There you are! See!' Mrs Cook cackled in triumph. 'You've gone and hurt yourself, haven't you?'

'No, it's just that I landed on my coccyx.'

The housekeeper gave me one of her more quizzical looks.

'I'VE BRUISED MY COCCYX!' I roared, as the good lady helped me to my feet.

For a moment, she seemed to give some serious consideration to what it was she thought she'd heard me say, then she shrugged her shoulders and dismissed it as highly improbable. 'As long as you haven't broken it,' she said, once again smiling broadly.

Once back in the porch I stood, massaging my rear end, as Patrick and I watched the ridiculously unstable little figure negotiating the hazardous stones with confident ease.

'Sure-footed as a mountain goat,' he commented, as she disappeared round the corner.

'Yes, amazing isn't it? Looking at her you wouldn't have thought she'd have got a yard without going over.'

'Like you, you mean?' he laughed.

'Yes, Patrick – just like me.'

'I know I shouldn't laugh, dear boy,' he went on. 'You did go an absolute purler, but it was spectacular.'

'Oh, good, I'm so glad.'

'I don't think I've ever seen footwork like it before:

your feet just kept shooting out from under you. The faster you got each one back on terra firma, the quicker it was gone again. You must have done half a dozen really immaculate high kicks before you eventually hit the ground. It really was a jolly entertaining performance, old boy.' He gave another noisy, giggling snort of laughter. 'You looked like a cross between a Bluebell Girl and a deranged cossack.'

'Thank you, Patrick,' I said. 'Shall we get on with the valuation now?'

We discovered The Lodge to be a labyrinth of strangely shaped rooms, winding staircases and dark cupboards. It had clearly not been substantially altered since it was built, and little modernisation had taken place either, although a central heating system had been installed at some point. As is usually the case, that particular improvement had left its mark on much of the furniture. The heat belched out by the huge cast-iron radiators had split and warped pieces in every room, and some of the best items had lost inlay and veneer. Despite that, the contents were still well worth selling, even though they were a little strange.

Like the hat collection in the hall, there was no great theme. It ranged from Egyptian tomb figures and good eighteenth century furniture to the sort of tourist souvenirs you would expect to find on Brighton pier.

Once we had sorted out the geography of the place, we split up to set about the valuation. Patrick was to handle all the furniture, rugs, clocks and bronzes while I was left with the remainder.

It was almost two hours later that we both found ourselves in the drawing room.

'How's it going?' he asked.

'Fine,' I replied, 'although I could do with some elevenses.'

'Me too. I wonder if the auditorially impaired Mrs Cook has sprinted back from the local hypermarket yet.'

'I haven't seen hide nor hair of her.'

'Nor me. Let's see what the place has to offer a couple of starving workers.'

Like the rest of the house, the kitchen hadn't changed substantially since the turn of the century. It was gloomy and cold, and there were no modern electrical appliances to be seen.

'Not so much as an electric kettle,' Patrick complained.

'It wouldn't do much good if there were,' I replied, 'the electricity's off – I checked earlier.'

'Oh, wonderful! That's the thing I hate about probate valuations – they're so bloody uncivilised. Give me a good cosy insurance valuation any day. House still lived in, central heating still on, grateful client providing non-stop tea and coffee. That's the life.'

'Yes,' I agreed, looking at the old, unlit range.

'Surely there must be some biscuits or something,' Patrick complained, as he set about searching through the ancient fitted cupboards which lined two sides of the room.

'It's no good,' he grumbled, at length. 'There's absolutely sod all here! The place looks as though it's been stripped by locusts.'

'Nuts!' I said.

'I beg your pardon?'

'There's a bowl of nuts in the dining room. I saw them earlier.'

'You're right! I saw them too. Come on, dear boy!'

It was all to no avail. A little dexterous use of the Victorian nutcrackers soon revealed the walnuts and brazils to be about the same vintage as the house itself. A few shrivelled kernels and a little blue-grey dust was all our best efforts could produce.

'Pathetic!' Patrick complained. 'I can remember the days when sideboards used to sag with the weight of the fruit bowls on them. I never could resist succulent fresh fruit. It always seemed quite wrong to let it go soggy and mouldy when I could give it a good home.'

'I do know what you mean,' I agreed. 'I've certainly helped to tidy up fruit bowls before now.'

'Exactly, waste not, want not,' he nodded. 'But then there's the problem of disposing of the evidence. What do you do with the apple-cores and orange peel?'

'Well, actually, I always chucked them on top of wardrobes and bookcases,' I confessed.

'A man after my own heart – once you've lobbed them over the cornice nobody's any the wiser.'

'That's right.'

'Yes,' he said, looking quite nostalgic, 'you know, the residues of past snacks of mine are probably still collecting dust, unseen, on top of some of the finest furniture in the country.'

I laughed. 'You've obviously eaten on better valuations than I have, Patrick.'

'Oh, not these days, dear boy. One's grateful for what one gets. But, in my formative years at Sothebys, I tossed my leftovers onto some super pieces.' The look of pure nostalgia returned. 'No doubt you know the story of the Sotheby's valuer and the nutshells?' he asked.

'No.'

'Oh, it's a classic. Probably apocryphal of course – I've heard it attributed to three different valuers over the years, but never mind.'

'What was supposed to have happened?'

'Well, the chap concerned was straight out of the top drawer. He knew his stuff, and could chat up the gentry. So, he was regarded as frontline material when it came to the really big stately home jobs. He had just one weakness: a passion for nuts. No sooner was he let loose in his client's marbled halls, than he'd set off in pursuit of the ducal nut bowl. Once he'd located it, he'd decimate the contents in a matter of minutes. It was supposed to be breath-taking to watch.'

196

'Extraordinary.'

'Certainly unusual, dear boy. Anyway, this habit left him with the old problem.'

'What to do with the shells?' I suggested.

'Spot on. There he'd be with a hundredweight or so of them and no safe means of disposal. If he threw them on top of a bookcase, half of them would probably tumble down the back and roll out onto the floor.'

'So, what did he do?'

'I'll tell you. He used to search out a major oil painting. You know the sort of thing – six foot by twelve foot, epic battle scene, vast panoramic landscape, huge Rubens women, something along those lines . . .'

'Yes.'

' . . . then he'd chuck the whole lot straight down the back of the picture.'

'He didn't!'

'Oh, yes, he did. And, of course, since any picture that isn't actually screwed into place, hangs away from the wall, the shells would rattle down behind the canvas like so much shrapnel, then they'd all end up safely wedged between the bottom of the frame and the wall. In the end, it became such a trademark of his that he used to make sure that he always chose the best picture in the place. I think he saw it as a sort of professional challenge.'

'Was he ever caught?'

'Not as such, but on one big job which had taken him several days, he did have a distinctly nasty moment. He was just bidding farewell to his elderly, aristocratic client, who was deigning to personally see him out, when they drew alongside some massive picture in the huge entrance hall. The old boy turned to our hero and asked him what he thought of the work. "It's a fine and important work, sir," he says. Then, just to be clever, he adds, "although it's a pity it has to be behind glass – it just catches the light, and the reflection detracts from its quality."

'Now, he only said that because he'd heard the old chap mention it on a couple of prior occasions. He was just icing the cake, but very nearly ended up over-egging the pudding, you see.'

'What happened?'

'On hearing his own opinion so accurately echoed back at him, the owner waxed eloquent on the best way of dealing with the problem. Then, suddenly, before our chap could do anything to stop him, the old fellow jumps forward, says, "if one could just angle it like this," and yanks the bottom of the frame away from the wall. Of course, there was this mighty cascade of shell fragments – four day's worth in all. On and on they went, pouring out and skating off across the marble floor. In a few moments they're all over the shop. The owner just stands there, open-mouthed, as if he'd just got the jackpot out of a one-armed bandit. Then, looking up at our man in total bewilderment, he says: "well, I'll be damned! How the devil d'you suppose that lot got there?"'

'What did he say?' I asked.

'Legend has it he replied – "Squirrels? Sir?".'

Patrick Faulkner and I went our separate ways once more. He in search of period pieces on the floors above, whilst I settled for whatever the butler's pantry had to offer.

It was hard to imagine what the downstairs areas of the house must have looked like in their heyday. Certainly, they would have been a long way removed from the damp, dirty and disused state that I found them in. Most of the cupboards and closets were empty save for a few old stoneware bottles, a collection of rusty smoothing irons and a large wooden flour bin.

There was no trace of the silver, on which the butler would have lavished so much time and attention, nor were there any large suites of glass or services of china. The cupboards were quite literally bare.

I perched myself on a table in the scullery, jotted down a figure to cover what little remained in the deserted warren of dreary rooms, then put down my pen and notebook.

It had been several years since I'd bought my first pipe and tobacco pouch. Now I was a committed pipe smoker and, as such, I required frequent doses of nicotine to enable me to do complicated things like thinking, talking, walking and breathing. Any prolonged separation from my pipe, or tobacco, or matches, or any combination of the three was guaranteed to produce a serious anxiety attack. Of course, in common with most smokers, and despite these clear symptoms of accute addiction, I insisted I could give up any time I chose. It was just that I didn't choose. After all, it was one of my few pleasures.

Musing on the likely whereabouts of The Lodge's china, glass and silver, I gripped the pipe between my teeth, struck a match, and drew hard as I put the flame to the bowl. At once there was a gurgling, slurping noise like an old water geyser being fired up, and my mouth filled with what tasted like burning creosote. I sprang from the table and spat the offending matter into the old sink in the corner of the room. To periodically get a mouthful of hot, tarry sludge is the lot of the pipe smoker. However, like most unpleasant things in life, its inevitability does nothing to make it more palatable when it actually happens. Still trying to evacuate the taste from my mouth, I tapped the remaining dottle from the pipe into the sink plughole. As it vanished from sight, Patrick Faulkner appeared in the doorway.

'Can you give me a hand for a moment, dear boy?' he asked.

'Yes, what's the problem?'

'I just want to check the cistern.'

'The cistern?'

'Yes, the one in the loo on the next floor landing.'

'This may sound a silly question,' I said, 'but, why?'

'Because,' he said, with a note of annoyance, 'I want to have a pee!'

'Oh, I see,' I said. 'You want to see if there's any water in it.'

'That's right. The water's off – I've already checked that – but as long as they haven't drained the cistern, I'm in business.'

It was the mark of a seasoned campaigner. Only once does any valuer use a lavatory in a strange house and then find that the water's off and the cistern's empty. The subsequent fruitless search for the stopcock; the panic stricken attempt to locate a garden rainwater butt; the trips upstairs with leaking buckets of murky water, all combine to create an experience so unforgettable that one never stumbles into the same trap twice. I followed my colleague up to the first-floor water closet.

'The problem is,' he said, pushing open the door, 'the height of the thing.'

I could see what he meant. The ancient cast iron cistern was fixed to the wall a good eight feet clear of the ground.

'I can just about reach it if I stand on the pan,' he went on, 'so if I take the lid off and pass it down to you, I can then stick my hand over the top to see if it's full.'

'Okay,' I replied, 'up you go.'

'Right, here goes!' He grabbed hold of the misshapen length of old piping that connected the cistern to the pan, then hauled himself up onto the wooden seat where he crouched for a moment. As he did so, every component of that fine example of the plumber's craft complained bitterly about the use it was being put to. The seat groaned, the lead piping sagged, and the cistern itself moved an inch or so away from the wall.

'Steady, Patrick,' I warned. 'I don't think it's very secure.'

'You're talking to a pro,' he said, very slowly straightening up to his full height. 'I know what I'm doing, dear boy. Never fear.'

He reached up to the cistern lid and tried to lift it. Nothing happened.

'Give it a bash,' I suggested, 'I expect it's pretty rusty.'

He thumped it several times with his hand, then tried to raise it again. Still nothing happened.

'Sod it!' he muttered, straining even harder. 'I will . . . shift this . . . damned thing . . .' He was beginning to go quite puce ' . . . if it's . . . the last thing . . . I . . . ' With a crash and a deluge of red-brown oxide, the lid of the cistern was suddenly free. So suddenly, that Hampson's Director of Furniture almost pitched backwards off his precarious perch. Swaying wildly, and covered in rust, he fought to regain his balance.

'Aaaaah!' he wailed, still waving the cistern cover above his head.

'Steady! Steady!' I called, quickly backing away. Although I wasn't sure which direction he was going to fall in, I was absolutely certain I didn't want it to be mine.

'Aaaaah!' he repeated.

'Hold on, Patrick!' I shouted.

From where he was teetering, my remark must have seemed singularly unhelpful. The only object he was actually holding on to at the time was the cistern lid, and there was no doubt that *his* chances of survival would be greatly enhanced if he let go of the thing. *Mine*, however, would be proportionately reduced, so I continued to urge tenacity – 'Hold on!'

As I cowered in the corner, almost behind the door, I watched in wonder and with not a little admiration as the big man, against all the odds, somehow managed to regain his balance.

'There,' he said, finally, with a self-confident smile, 'that's better. I must say, for one moment there, I thought I was going to . . . aaaaah . . .!'

The old wooden seat had taken all it could. With a

crack like a pistol shot it split in two and gave way. Patrick, all hope and footing gone, responded to the irresistible demands of gravity, and dropped like a stone. Ending slumped against the wall, one foot on the floor, the other deep in the pan, he miraculously still retained his grip on the cistern lid.

'Shall I take it from you?' I asked. They were my last words before I collapsed with laughter.

'Oh, very funny!' he snarled. 'Ha, bloody, ha!'

'I'm sorry,' I gasped, 'but you do look . . .'

'And so will you if you don't take this sodding lump of scrap from me. NOW!'

'All right, all right,' I said, 'don't panic. I've got it.' I took the lid from him and put it down against the wall.

'Panic! I like that,' he grumbled, holding onto my shoulder to steady himself as he extricated his right foot from the watery depths of the pan. 'I wasn't the one quivering and whimpering in the corner.'

'No, Patrick, you were the one with the foot in the lavatory pan.'

He glared at me for a moment then turned his attention to the foot in question. Pulling off his shoe, he emptied the water it contained back into the pan.

'Look at my bloody Gucci,' he complained, holding up the soiled fashion object for me to inspect. 'It's probably ruined.'

'It's only a little water.'

'It's all right for you – it's not your bloody shoe,' he muttered, removing his sock and wringing it out into the pan before putting it on again. 'And just in case you've forgotten, I still haven't had a pee and I still don't know whether or not there's any water in that sodding cistern.'

'Get out of the way and I'll check,' I said.

He hobbled backwards, still trying to put his sock on, and I took my turn to scale the heights of the wobbling, rattling contraption.

'Well?' Patrick asked, impatiently, as I reached into the cistern.

'Dry as a bone I'm afraid.'

'Oh, great! Just great! They've drained the whole system. I'll have to go in the garden. There's nothing else for it.'

Descending the main staircase at some speed, my colleague seemed oblivious to the discomfort caused by having a seriously damp Gucci. His mind was now monopolised by a more urgent and compelling matter.

'I'll go out this way,' he said, bounding across the hall and through the door to the kitchens. 'There's certain to be some heavy cover at the back . . . hold on, what's that smell?'

I stood and sniffed the air for a moment. 'Smoke,' I said, 'but where the hell's it coming from?'

'In there!' he called out, pointing through the open door to the scullery. 'The bloody sink's on fire!'

And, unlikely though it was, when I joined Patrick in the doorway, tongues of flame were indeed licking up out of the plughole. It couldn't be described as a serious fire, and it was obviously safely contained, but both of us stood staring at it, mesmerised by the sheer improbability of its origin.

'How the devil could that happen?' Patrick said, scratching his head, his thoughts temporarily diverted from his pressing problem.

'I cannot tell a lie,' I said, 'I am the one who set the U-bend on fire. It must have been drained years ago and got filled up with rubbish.'

'But, how could it catch alight, just like that . . . ' He stopped in mid-sentence, his expression changing in a moment from one of confusion to one of panic, ' . . . no good . . . must go . . . back in a minute . . . ' And with that, leaving the door open behind him, he dashed from the scullery, across the yard and off towards the garden.

As the flames flickered away to nothing in the

plughole, I recalled that I hadn't replaced the cistern lid upstairs. I retraced my steps through the hallway and began, once again, to climb the stairs.

About halfway up, where the staircase doubled back on itself, there was a landing with a large window inset with stained glass panels. It overlooked a fair proportion of the property, including the partially-walled wilderness which must once have been the kitchen garden. As I stood there gazing out on the sad, derelict scene, an equally sad sight came into view. It was Patrick, apparently still in search of adequate cover.

He was moving in a strange way: slightly stooped, hands clasped low in front of him, not walking and yet not running either. I suppose it was a sort of trot, but he looked as though his knees were tied together, and that gave him the appearance of somebody about to break into the Charleston. Looking hither and thither, searching and questing the whole time as he hopped, skipped and *chasséd* down the old brick path by the high wall, he was clearly in some distress.

His problem was a continuous line of ramblers which bordered one side of the path, and which had long since developed into an impenetrable barrier. This meant that the path was now completely cut off from the garden. There was just no way for my unfortunate colleague to get through.

Whether, at that point, he finally grasped the hopelessness of his task or whether the physical strain simply proved more than he could bear, I don't know, but as I watched he suddenly gave up looking for a hiding place and just turned his face to the wall.

From my vantage point I had already seen the ramshackle little door in the wall. It was only a few yards further on from where Patrick was standing but was in such a poor state that I had assumed it was no longer in use. I was wrong. No sooner had Patrick succumbed to nature's irresistible demands, than the door opened.

For all I know it may well have been Mrs Cook's daily practice to leave by the front gate and to return via the kitchen garden. Or, perhaps, she had just decided to use the back path because of the dangerous condition of the other one earlier that morning. Whatever her reasons for being there, there was no mistaking the rocking, rolling, dumpy little form of the housekeeper as she stepped onto the red brick path and turned to close the door behind her.

Standing there on the staircase, I felt strangely helpless. Although I was the only member of the trio who was aware of the intense little drama being played out in the garden, I was totally unable to influence its course, let alone actually prevent what appeared to be the pre-ordained, disastrous dénouement. Examined in that cool, logical light, my only sensible course of action appeared to be to sit back and enjoy the show.

Down below, the two leading players were as yet happily ignorant of each other's presence. Mrs Cook was still shuffling about dealing with the old door, and Patrick Faulkner was a picture of joy and content-ment. Legs slightly apart, hands behind his back, head thrown back, looking at the blue sky with its thin, hazy cloud. For the moment he was in another world.

Mrs Cook must have seen him as soon as she stepped out of the doorway alcove onto the path. Deaf she may have been, but blind she was not. Anyway, regardless of what she did or did not see, rocking wildly from one bandy pin to the other, she advanced on Patrick without displaying any obvious sign of concern. I saw her briefly address some remark to him in passing, and then, without even breaking her stride, she continued on her rolling way towards the house.

I doubt that a couple of thousand volts would have caused Patrick Faulkner to jump any higher than he did when Mrs Cook spoke to him. As she went on her way, he was left in a near state of collapse, leaning against the wall, fumbling with his clothing.

'You mean you saw what happened out there?' he said, when he had returned to the house.

'Yes, and may I say that your attempt to clear the garden wall was one of the most spectacular vaults without the aid of a pole that I have ever seen.'

'You are still within your trial period at Hampson's I believe, Mr Harton,' he replied, coolly.

'It's all right, Patrick,' I said, 'I'll never breathe a word of it to a soul . . . on just one condition.'

'Which is?'

'You tell me what it was Mrs Cook said to you.'

He grinned. 'You wouldn't believe me if I did.'

'Try me.'

'Well, I still don't know whether she knew what it was I was doing out there, but if she did, all I can say is she's got a sense of humour.'

'Why, what was it she said?'

'Would you believe – "nice out now, i'n't it, Mr Fuller"?'

'Despite the little mishaps, a worthwhile day's work I think,' Patrick Faulkner remarked, as we drove back towards London.

'It certainly was,' I agreed, 'especially since it's all coming in for sale.'

'Yes, we don't get houses like that very often now. It may have been a bit cranky but I don't think the contents have changed much since 1900.'

'Except for the table silver, dinner services and glass – not a sign of it. I suppose it was all sold at some stage.'

'Not at all, not at all, dear boy. It's all safely stashed at Bailey's by now. Though when I say safely, I use the word in its least literal sense.'

'I don't understand – why's it at Bailey's.'

206

'For reasons now lost in the mists of time the stuff was put into store during the last war. I understand there's quite a bit of junk amongst it so I've had it all shipped to Bailey's for sorting – they've got more room than we have at the moment. You can pop down there, value it, select the stuff for us and get that transferred to Vanbrugh Street. The rubbish can stay in store at Bailey's until probate's granted then they can sell it.'

'Good. I'll go down there tomorrow,' I said.

'Excellent. By the way, have you come across Frank Parsons yet.'

'Who?'

'Francis George Parsons, cataloguer extraordinaire and king of the smalls at Bailey's saleroom.'

'No,' I said, 'I can't say I have.'

'In that case, have an early night, old chap. You'll need your wits about you tomorrow.'

Chapter 14

'Hello, Mr H,' Harry Sutton greeted me. 'What brings you all the way out here when there's no sale on?'

'Morning, Harry,' I replied. 'I've come to have a look at the stuff from Blackwood.'

'Blackwood? Blackwood?' he muttered, stroking his chin. 'You've got me there, Mr Harton. I don't recall anything coming in from any place called Blackwood.'

'It actually came in from store,' I explained. 'It's a probate lot – in the name of Carr deceased.'

Harry Sutton continued to look puzzled. 'What was it exactly, Mr H?' he asked.

'Silver, ceramics and glass.'

'Oh, I know the lot you mean! It came in a couple of days ago. I think there was getting on for nearly twenty tea chests of the stuff – something to do with Mr Faulkner.'

'That's the lot,' I said. 'I've got to go through it and select the pieces for Hampson's, and then you can sell the rest.'

'Oh, I see,' Harry said, smiling amiably. 'It's not all for us then?'

'No, no, Patrick Faulkner just thought it would be easier to sort it here than at Vanbrugh Street – we're pressed for space there at the moment.'

'I see,' he repeated, 'I see.'

Although he was still smiling benignly, I thought there was just the faintest flicker of nervousness behind

208

that set grin. I recalled encountering it before, when I'd discovered the Regency breakfast table in the middle of the stack of household furniture.

'Is there a problem, Harry?'

'Problem! No, no problem, Mr Harton,' he assured me, 'but . . .'

'But?'

'But . . . well . . . it would have been helpful if Mr Faulkner had explained that some of the stuff was going to Hampson's.'

'I thought he had.'

'No, well, not to me anyway, and I'm pretty certain he didn't mention it to Frank either.'

'That's Frank Parsons?' I said.

For a moment he looked surprised that I should need to ask, then he struck his forehead with the palm of his hand. 'Cor blimey, Mr Harton, I keep forgetting you've never met Frank, have you?'

'No, he's never been about when I've been here.'

'No, he's in and out a lot, is Frank. In and out a lot.'

'Is he in this morning?'

'This morning? Oh, yes, he's in this morning. Definitely in this morning.'

'Good.'

'Oh, yes . . . definitely.'

Harry Sutton stood nodding his head enthusiastically. He was still smiling but the nervousness was still there too. For some reason he didn't seem to be in any great rush for me to make the long awaited acquaintance of Frank Parsons.

'Shall I go straight up, then?' I asked.

'Er . . . well . . . I'll come with you, shall I, Mr Harton? Then I can, sort of, introduce you properly.'

'Fine – let's go.'

'Yes, let's go,' Harry agreed, both feet remaining firmly planted on the floor.

'Are you sure there's no problem, Harry?'

'No, no, no, no, no,' he assured me, 'it's just that . . . well, it's just that Frank's got his own way of doing things.'

'I'm sure he has.'

'And they might seem a little bit . . . a little bit . . . well . . . a little bit . . .'

'Unorthodox?' I suggested.

'Yes, that's it, Mr H. You've put it in a nutshell – Frank's a bit unorthodox.'

'That's all right, Harry,' I said. 'I realised on my first visit here that the staff at Bailey's are pioneers when it comes to unusual systems of stock handling.'

Harry Sutton shifted his weight from one foot to the other and looked concerned. 'You mean the Regency breakfast table, Mr H?'

'Good Lord, no, Harry,' I said, putting an arm round his shoulder, 'nothing so specific . . . but since you mention it . . .'

'Now I thought I'd explained about that, Mr Harton . . .'

'And so you did, Harry. So you did.'

'It was just one of them things, sir.'

'So it was, Harry, and it went very well in the next sale anyway.'

'It did that, Mr H – two thousand, eight hundred pounds! Well, you could've knocked me down with a feather.'

'I don't doubt it. But the point I'm making is that whatever Frank Parsons gets up to . . . I'm sorry, I'll rephrase that . . . whatever system Frank Parsons employs, I'm sure I won't be surprised by it.'

Although Harry nodded in agreement, his manner still suggested he was not altogether convinced. Nevertheless, he manfully steeled himself against whatever might follow and led the way upstairs.

It must be said that my impression on entering Frank Parsons' domain was not a favourable one. Just like the

210

ground floor, the first floor of Bailey's was scruffy, dirty and chaotic. It appeared to be a single, sizeable room with a partitioned-off area in one corner. Very little natural light penetrated the grimy window panes, and that which did was largely eclipsed by the heavily laden tiers of shelving that occupied three of the four walls and obstructed every window in the place. As a counter measure, a number of neon tubes, dangling from fluff-covered chains, fizzed and buzzed above us, casting their bilious light over all. Looking round me, I estimated from the depth of dust on some of the items that they had been there for a very long time.

Unwholesome and undesirable though all this certainly was, it was no worse than I had expected. This left me wondering just why Harry Sutton had been so apprehensive about my introduction to the Frank Parsons' System.

'I know it looks a bit chaotic, Mr H,' he observed, 'but without a word of a lie, Frank can always put his hand on any bit you want. He's better than a computer he is.'

A double row of old, splintery trestle tables stood in the middle of the room. Surrounded by empty tea chests and discarded newspaper packing, they sagged under the weight of a large collection of china and glass.

'This must be the Carr estate consignment,' I said. 'But there should be some silver in here somewhere. Where would that be, Harry?'

'Silver?'

'Yes.'

'Er, well, I don't rightly know, but I expect Frank's put it somewhere safe.'

'Let's ask him, shall we?' I suggested.

'Yes, yes,' Harry agreed, 'we'll ask him. I expect he's in the office.'

The office – the partitioned area in the corner of the room – turned out to be a miniaturised version of the rest of the first floor. Its only concession to being described as an office was that it contained a heavily scratched oak desk and chair, and a battered green filing cabinet. Otherwise, it was a muddle of shelving, boxes, tea chests and goods for sale. In the middle of it all sat a grey-haired figure. He wore heavy framed spectacles, a brown apron, and had his shirt sleeves rolled up above his elbows. He didn't look up as we entered but continued to pore over some papers in front of him on the desk.

'Blimey, Frank,' Harry said, looking at him, 'aren't you cold without a jacket?'

'I got that,' Parsons grunted, pointing down to a single bar electric fire, without even glancing in our direction.

'It'd still be a bit nippy for me, mate,' Harry said, persisting with his chattiness.

Frank Parsons did not reply.

'Frank, this is Mr Harton, who takes our sales now. You remember – I mentioned him.'

This time Frank Parsons stopped reading and slowly looked up. Hooded by his shaggy, grizzled eyebrows, and framed by the horn-rimmed glasses, his eyes appeared large and almost black. He stared at me, malevolently, for some moments, then, without uttering a word, he nodded slowly and turned back to his correspondence.

'Mr Harton's come to have a look at that stuff what Mr Faulkner had sent in the other day,' Harry continued, in a doggedly cheerful tone.

Immediately, Parsons looked up again.

'Why's that?' he asked Harry, as though I either wasn't there or couldn't answer for myself.

'Because the better pieces are going to be sold at Hampson's,' I said. 'Of course, everything else can be offered here.'

'Faulkner didn't say anything about that to me,' Parsons complained, still addressing Harry Sutton.

212

'No, that's what I said to Mr Harton,' Harry agreed, 'but there it is – Mr Harton's in charge of it all now, and he's got to go through it to pick out what's to go to Vanbrugh Street.'

Frank Parsons gave me another unfriendly look and returned his attention to his desk. 'He'd better get on with it then,' he muttered, over his shoulder.

'Where's the silver?' I asked.

'What silver?' Parsons replied, studying yet another piece of paperwork.

'The silver that's supposed to have come in with the other pieces out there on those tables,' I said, gesturing to the main room.

'I haven't seen any silver.'

'Have all the tea chests been unpacked?' I asked, as my hostility to the surly Parsons mounted.

'Don't know, really.'

'Have you got a list of what's supposed to be there?'

'No.'

'Well, how many tea chests were there?'

'Didn't count them.'

'Harry,' I said, to the increasingly agitated head porter.

'Yes, Mr H.'

'A word, please.'

He followed me out of the office.

'Harry,' I continued, 'I want you to listen carefully to what I'm about to say.'

'Yessir.'

'I'm going to start sorting through the pieces that have been unpacked on those tables.'

'Yessir.'

'And within the next five minutes I expect you to bring me any tea chests that have not yet been unpacked . . .'

'Yessir.'

' . . . including those containing the silver . . .'

'Yessir.'

213

'. . . and . . .'

'Yessir?'

'. . . any individual pieces that have already been unpacked and have . . .' I paused and chose my words with care, '. . . shall we say . . . been put away overnight for safekeeping.'

'Yessir,' Harry said, turning on his heel and heading back towards Frank Parsons' inner sanctum, 'I shan't keep you a minute, Mr H.'

As I removed my jacket, rolled up my sleeves and began the laborious but fascinating task of selecting and listing the pieces for Hampson's, I could hear a muffled but lively discussion taking place in the office. A few moments later, Harry reappeared with a large tray groaning with porcelain.

'You were right, you know, Mr Harton,' he said, once again beaming, 'there's two chests of silver and plated stuff in the office and a couple more trays of china to come out.'

'You don't say?'

'I do, Mr H. You were spot on. The lads must have put it all in there for safe keeping when Frank was out yesterday.'

'How thoughtful of them.'

'Yes, but I don't know how much of it's any good, of course. They don't know much about china.'

'Oh, they seem to have a pretty good instinct for it,' I said, picking up one of a pair of plates. They were painted with botanical subjects, and I knew I would find gold anchor marks on them when I turned them over.

'Are they good, then?' Harry asked, with all the innocence of a convent novice.

'Chelsea,' I replied, 'circa 1758.'

'Well, I'm blowed!'

By the time Frank Parsons' office had disgorged all the Carr estate items it was protecting, I had a good collection of porcelain and glass, a few pieces of silver

214

and some nice old Sheffield Plate which would enhance several Hampson catalogues.

I found Harry Sutton seated in his own shambolic office when I went back downstairs. He was looking unusually pensive but he brightened up immediately when I entered.

'A worthwhile visit, Mr H?'

'Very, Harry. In more ways than one.'

'Yes?'

'Yes, Harry. I think you and I should have a little chat; don't you?'

'Yes?'

I nodded and pulled up a chair. 'Let me tell you a fairy tale, Harry.'

'A fairy tale, sir?'

'A fairy tale. It goes like this: once upon a time there was a wicked porcelain cataloguer. He worked all on his own at the top of a great big auction rooms, and he was the only one who knew what really went on in his department.'

Harry Sutton's fixed smile remained firmly in place but he shifted uneasily in his seat.

'Now, this wicked porcelain cataloguer used to do all sorts of naughty things, but by far the naughtiest was what he used to do with probate lots. Do you know, he used to cream off some of the best pieces and keep them in his office. He'd keep them there for a very long time, so that if a solicitor or beneficiary wrote or called to ask what had happened to the late Mr Carr's Chelsea plates, for instance, he would reach up, take them off the shelf and say: "Here they are. We weren't sure who they belonged to so we were waiting for them to be claimed." If however, nobody claimed them, then he would eventually spirit them away, sell them and pocket the dosh.'

Harry Sutton's smile had vanished. He looked at me, wide-eyed, then cleared his throat nervously. 'Are you saying that Frank Parsons is . . .'

'I'm not saying anything, Harry. As I told you, it was just a fairy tale.'

His smile slowly began to return.

'However, if I found anybody, and I mean *anybody*, getting up to that sort of game with property belonging to my clients, the next time they sing in their baths, it'll be as sopranos. I trust I make myself clear, Harry?'

'As crystal, sir.'

'Good.'

As I got up to go, Harry Sutton suddenly leapt to his feet, dashed round the desk, grasped my hand and shook it enthusiastically.

'You don't know what a weight you've just taken off my mind, Mr Harton. You will never know what a relief this is for me.'

'Yes, all right, Harry . . .'

'Until now,' he dropped his voice to a whisper and shot furtive glances about the office, 'it was just me against them, but now you're involved . . .'

'Yes, I get the picture . . .'

' . . . now you're involved I can put an end to it . . .'

'Harry!'

'Yessir.'

'Don't say another word.'

'Right, sir. My lips are sealed.'

I wrested my hand from his grip and turned to go.

'Oh, just one more thing, Mr H,' he said.

'What's that, Harry?'

'In your fairy tale . . .'

'Yes.'

' . . . did they all live happily ever after?'

'Do you think Harry Sutton's really tried to stop the fiddling at Bailey's?' Charlotte asked.

'What fiddling?'

'The fiddling you've just been talking about – the silver and porcelain – and then there was the Regency table.'

'And what proof have you that they weren't just mislaid as Harry said?'

'Oh, come on! You don't think they were mislaid.'

'Perhaps not, but I don't *know* they weren't.'

'Anyway, you haven't answered my question,' Charlotte persisted. 'Do you think Harry Sutton's in on any fiddles that *might* be taking place?'

'Well, unless I've completely misjudged the man,' I replied, 'I would think not a single thing happens at Bailey's without Harry Sutton knowing about it.'

'So you *do* think he's in on all the swindles?'

'Swindles?'

'Oooh!'

'I suspect he takes his commission on any transactions that take place, yes.'

'That's awful.'

'Yes.'

'But you still like him, don't you?'

'Yes, I do – he's a character.'

'Which makes it all right?'

'No, but it does make it much more fun,' I said. 'And I think Harry will keep them in line down there now, when it comes to Hampson's business, anyway.'

'That's what you said before.'

'I know, but that was before my skirmish with Frank Parsons. Now we've met, I don't think he'll be quite as ready to try it on next time.'

'And if he does?'

'Then he'll be finished if I have any say in the matter.'

'I take it Mr Parsons doesn't qualify in your book as "a character", then?'

'Oh, yes, he's a character all right – an extremely unpleasant one.'

Charlotte was about to reply when she obviously remembered something. 'Oh!' she said, 'I almost forgot, Bob Derby wants to talk to you about arranging the first of these solicitors' lunches. And Bernard Thornton came crashing in here this morning.'

'What did he want?'

'I'm not entirely sure. He said something about snuff boxes and that you'd be interested. Unfortunately, I wasn't really listening. I was too busy concentrating on saving the coffee percolator and picking up all the papers from the tray that he'd knocked off your desk.'

'Oh, you mean he crashed in literally?'

'You bet. I do like Bernard – he's a very kind-hearted man – but I really think he must be the least co-ordinated person I've ever met. He lurched around in here for about ten minutes this morning and very nearly wrecked the place. How it is he never breaks anything in the Ceramics Department I'll never know.'

'No, it's amazing,' I agreed. 'He was perfectly safe when I took him on that valuation too. I think it's all psychological.'

'You may be right,' Charlotte said. 'All I know is that it takes a long time to clear up after one of his visits.'

I decided I would pop next door to see Bob Derby and Bernard rather than telephone them. I usually found Derby slightly less intimidating face to face than he was on the telephone, and visits to the Ceramics Department were always entertaining.

'Come in.' As usual, the Chairman's voice sounded distracted and just a little irritable when he answered my knock.

'Ah, Richard,' he said, brightening up as I entered his office, 'how are things going?'

'Not too badly,' I replied.

'Picked up a good lot in Surrey the other day I understand.'

'Yes, but it was down to Patrick Faulkner rather than me.'

'Yes, so I understand,' he grinned. 'Not the sort of detail that Patrick would be likely to forget to mention to me I can assure you. Never mind, at least I know the whole job will be properly co-ordinated for once. I understand you had your first run-in with Frank Parsons this morning – well done.'

'News travels fast,' I said.

'Oh yes. You've obviously got them rattled down there. I've had Harry Sutton on the telephone singing your praises.'

'Goodness!'

'As Mae West said, "Goodness had nothing to do with it". That call amounted to a strategic realignment on Harry's part. He obviously thinks you're a force to be reckoned with. Keep the pressure up and you'll have them eating out of your hand before long.'

'Right.'

'Now, have you managed to come up with a list of solicitors for these lunches yet?'

'Not yet, I'm afraid.'

'Never mind. My girl, Rachel, has sorted out the first guest list and arranged for the caterers. We can use some of our own staff as waitresses. Have a word with Charlotte, she'll do for one. She's hardly rushed off her feet at the moment.'

'Er . . .'

'What's this – hesitation from the man who bearded Frank Parsons in his den? Don't tell me you're frightened of a mere slip of a girl.'

'No, it's just that I don't think she's going to be very keen on the idea.'

'I don't want her to be keen. I want her to be a waitress.'

'Well, I'll certainly ask . . .'

'You do what you like, Richard. Charlotte Morrison's down on the list. If she doesn't like it, she can do the other thing.'

'When's it arranged for?' I asked, seeing there was no point arguing with him.

'End of March sometime. Ask Rachel. She'll give you all the details.'

'Okay.'

'Anything else?' he said, looking at his watch.

'I don't think so.'

'Good. Ask Rachel to step in as you go out, please.'

Bernard Thornton appeared unusually smart, although rather vacant as he leaned against the first floor reception desk. He was wearing an immaculate blue pin-stripe suit, and was holding a plastic cup, full of coffee, a few inches from his mouth as he stared blankly out of the window. He didn't notice my arrival.

'Hello, Bernard.'

'Mmmmm?' As he turned, the coffee splashed onto his hand and jacket. 'Blast!' he said, putting the cup down and pulling a handkerchief out of his sleeve to dry himself off.

'Sorry, did I make you jump?'

'No, my fault – I was miles away. How are you, Richard? What can I do for you?'

'I'm not sure. Charlotte said you wanted to speak to me about something.'

'I did?' he looked puzzled. 'Oh, yes, of course I did! I remember. It was about that business with the snuff boxes. You know – what was the old girl's name?'

'Mrs Randolph-Bruce.'

'That's right – nice old bird. I liked her.'

'Have you been to Whitecliffe?'

'Yes, I was there yesterday, so I paid a visit to Harbour Antiques. I don't suppose you've managed to get in to see the old girl's friend, have you?'

'I'm afraid not. Mrs Randolph-Bruce was right. Kitty does not want to know.'

'Oh, well, in that case I'm doubly pleased that I called on Harbour Antiques yesterday.'

'What was the place like?' I asked.

'Just what I expected,' Bernard replied, still dabbing away absent-mindedly at the damp patch on his jacket. 'One or two bits of silver and some nineteenth-century copper and brassware, but chiefly a load of modern, continental dross. It's more a souvenir shop than an antiques emporium. I'm surprised they don't sell plastic buckets and spades.'

'Any sign of the snuff boxes?'

'A few remnants, but not many. The character who runs the place offered to take my telephone number and call me when he gets the next consignment.'

'What was he like?'

'Oh, he was just a little mouse of a man. He's no international criminal, I can assure you of that.' Bernard gave his jacket a final dab, then stuffed his handkerchief back into his sleeve. 'Come to that,' he continued, 'he's no authority on snuff boxes either. From the way he'd priced the ones in the shop he hasn't got a clue what they are or what they're worth. Generally speaking, he'd overpriced the rubbish and underpriced the better ones – not that there were any really interesting ones there.'

'Already sold them, I expect.'

'Almost certainly. I would think he's got one or two regular buyers who think it's Christmas every time he gives them a call. They sprint along to Harbour Antiques, pick up the gems at giveaway prices and leave our friend with the scraps.'

'So, you don't think there's any great conspiracy afoot?'

'No, the man's too much of a bloody idiot to conspire about anything. He's so thick, he should be selling rock with "MORON" running right through it.'

'What about the daughter?' I asked. 'Did you see anything of her?'

'Did I. I should think I did!' He winced at the thought. 'There's no doubt that she's the *éminence grise* in the whole business. Your Mrs Randolph-hyphen-thingummyjig was spot-on there: Gloria is an absolute powerhouse.'

'Gloria?'

'Yes, in excelsis – she must stand at least six feet tall. I'd just got used to dealing with the pathetic little boyfriend when Gloria appeared on the scene. Hand on heart, Richard, she scared me half to death. No wonder she changes her husbands so frequently. A couple of years with Gloria and you'd be nothing more than a dried up husk . . . an empty tank . . . a burnt out shell . . .'

'Er, Bernard . . .'

'Sorry, sorry, you must forgive me. I was fantasising. It's just that there's something terribly addictive about raw, cold fear. If she'd got between me and the door, I swear I wouldn't have got out with my trousers intact.'

'Bernard, I think you're fantasising again.'

'Sorry! Now, where was I? Oh, yes . . . in she came and started talking about the snuff boxes and asking me if I was a collector since I seemed to know so much about them.' He paused. 'I suppose it's fair to say that I was probably laying it on a bit thick by that time.'

'Really? You surprise me.'

'Well, it wasn't really my fault if she interpreted my words as meaning that I was an authority on the subject,' he said. 'Anyway, I bought a couple of boxes – not particularly wonderful examples, but probably the only two left which weren't too expensive. Then I just couldn't resist it.'

'You couldn't resist what?'

'It was seeing that statuesque Diana standing next to that pathetic little apology for a man that made me do it.'

'Made you do what, Bernard?' I asked.

'Well, Richard, I told her that one of the boxes I'd just bought – a very basic little nineteenth century silver-mounted horn job – was almost certainly American. And that, as such, it was worth at least a couple of thousand pounds.'

'And what had you paid for it?'

'Let's just say I had change from thirty quid.'

'And, I take it, it wasn't American.'

222

'Good Lord, no! No, it's as English as we are. I just did it for the hell of it. It was pure malevolence on my part. I just wanted to see if she would strike him dead with a single blow.'

'And did she?'

'No, I think she decided that would be too good for him. I'm fairly certain his death is going to be slow and unbelievably painful. What a way to go!' he concluded wistfully.

'Bernard, I had no idea you harboured these masochistic tendencies.'

'Oh, yes, but only when it comes to really big women.' He gulped down the last of the coffee and tossed the cup into the wastepaper bin below the counter. 'But then, we all have our little weaknesses,' he concluded, as he turned to go.

'One last question,' I said. 'Why so smart? You look like an advertisement for Savile Row.'

'Ignoring the implication that I usually resemble the contents of a dustbin, thank you for the compliment. And, in answer to your question, I'm off to see an important client in half an hour. All being well, I should return with half a dozen really good pieces. Keep your fingers crossed for me.'

'I will,' I said, and headed back to my office.

The business of the snuff boxes still rankled. The thought of a good and fairly valuable collection being split up and sold for a fraction of its true worth was very frustrating. But these things happened, and all too frequently. I knew that. In the end it was up to Mrs Randolph-Bruce's friend, and since she wouldn't help herself, we couldn't help her either. It was just one of those things.

'A waitress! You have to be joking!' Charlotte's complexion was fast approaching the colour of her hair.

'No, I'm not joking . . .'

'And you agreed to it?'

'Not exactly, no, I . . .'

'Well, what exactly did you say?'

'I said I would ask you . . .'

'Oh, yes, and what did you say you'd do if I said no?'

I shrugged my shoulders. 'You know him better than I do,' I protested. 'You know there's no point in arguing with him once he's got a bee in his bonnet about something. It's much better to just let the dust settle and then . . .'

'The dust isn't going to settle!' she shouted. 'Not until you make it clear to Robert-bloody-Derby that I'm your secretary and personal assistant, not some McDonald's burger-bar reject.'

'You're over-reacting.'

'I AM *NOT* OVER-REACTING!' she shrieked. 'I've worked for this company for a year and a half. In that time I've never once refused to do whatever grotty job they stuck me with, but I WILL *NOT* BE A WAITRESS! If Derby insists, he can stick his job up his . . .'

'All right! I'll speak to him again.'

'I don't care what you do – I'm not going to be . . .'

'Yes, all right!' I shouted. 'I have got the message – you're not going to be a waitress.'

Five minutes later I was back outside the Chairman's door.

'Come in!' This time there was far less distraction but a great deal more irritation in the voice.

I opened the door and was greeted by a waft of Havana cigar smoke. Charles Morrison-Whyte was sitting opposite Bob Derby.

'I'm sorry. I didn't know you were busy,' I said.

'That's all right, as long as whatever it is is brief,' Derby replied.

'Yes, well . . . er . . . I'll come back later I think.'

'As you wish.'

'Yes – it'll keep.'

Charlotte was sitting at her desk, arms folded defiantly. 'Well, what did he say?'

'He told me to be brief.'

'And were you?'

'Extremely – I came straight back here.'

'Richard! You are pathetic!'

'Oh, no, I'm not. I'll have you know that a certain director was with him when I blundered in. A certain director who would be unlikely to support your case.'

'CMW?'

'The very same. And I seem to remember you telling me, not long ago, that Charles Morrison-Whyte had once referred to you as "a cocky little madam".'

'Yes.'

'So, perhaps you'll let me handle this in my own way and in my own time.'

'Oh, all right,' she said, reluctantly, 'but I'm not going to be a . . .'

'Charlotte!'

'All right! Just as long as you know – I'll walk out before I lower myself to that.'

Chapter 15

'But it would only be for a week.'

'But it's such short notice.'

'But it's only for a week,' Sarah repeated. 'And you admitted that you're not exactly working flat-out yet.'

'I know,' I said, 'but I've only been with Hampson's for just over two months – it's pushing my luck to take a week's holiday at this stage.'

'Not at all. Now's the time to take a break. Once things hot up you won't have time to get away.'

'Oh, I don't know.'

'Come on, it'll be fun. You don't know what you're missing. You've never lived till you've skied.'

Her enthusiasm was certainly very persuasive. But it just wasn't that simple to drop everything and take off at a few days' notice.

'I don't have any equipment,' I said.

'Doesn't matter. Hire a ski suit from Moss Bros at Covent Garden, and then hire boots and skis out there, at the resort.'

'You make it all sound very easy.'

'Please come with us, Richard. It will be fun – I promise.'

I nodded to the bored-looking waiter as he hovered with the coffee. 'Another liqueur?' I asked Sarah.

'No thanks, just some more coffee.'

The waiter topped up our cups and glided away.

'So what do you say?' my companion continued her offensive.

'Oh, all right,' I capitulated. 'I'll see what Bob Derby says.'

'Great! And you'll ask this friend of yours as well?'

'Yes, I'll ask him, but I certainly can't promise that he'll be able to come at this sort of notice. He's bound to be busier than . . .'

Any further protests were cut short by Sarah as she suddenly leant across the table and kissed me.

'Now let me get this straight,' Philip said, holding up a hand to stop my sales patter. 'You're inviting me to go on a skiing holiday, which is going to cost me an arm and a leg – perhaps literally, since I've never skied in my life before. I'll be with a bunch of people I don't know from Adam. And I won't have time to get fit because we'd be leaving in just a few days' time. I mean, that is the proposition, is it, Richard?'

'Yes,' I said, dispiritedly. Put like that, and that was the only way to put it, it did sound ludicrous.

'Okay.'

'What?'

'Okay – I'm game.'

'Really?'

'Yes, why not. I'm due some holiday, I've got no sale that week and I'll be back in good time for the silver sale at the end of the month. Let's go for it.'

'That's tremendous,' I said. 'Now, all I've got to do is choose the right moment to ask Bob Derby about taking that week off myself.'

'Well, if I were you, I'd get in there and see him right away. He was up here earlier saying nice things about you.'

'This is very worrying. He's full of compliments at the moment, and I still haven't done anything yet.'

'I don't find anything remarkable about that,' Philip

said, languidly leaning back in his chair and putting one foot on his desk. 'In my experience, that's the only time one ever gets any worthwhile recognition.'

'You think so?'

'Oh, yes. Immediately you actually start doing something you're bound to upset somebody, then the sky falls in. No, my theory is keep your head down, do nothing controversial – which means do nothing at all – and accept the plaudits of the great and the good. It's the only way.'

'You reckon that works, do you?'

'Of course it does. The only snag is you have to change your job every three years.'

'Why's that?'

'Because, any longer than that and they find you out. It's never wise to outstay one's welcome I always think.'

'I'll try to remember that,' I replied.

'You do that. Now what's all this business about solicitors' lunches?'

'Why? Have you been roped in to them?'

'Sure have. The first one's due to coincide with my good silver sale, so I've got to give the honoured guests a little talk on a couple of the better lots then join you all for the bunfight.'

'Well, lucky old you.'

'Yes,' he said, 'I can hardly wait. Not that I had any choice in the matter, of course. Bob was in best jack-boot form this morning – no objections, no answering back, no suggestions. The only thing he wanted to hear about was how to make Hampson's even bigger and better. And, just at the moment, he's convinced that you and your department are the secret weapons.'

'I wish I shared his confidence,' I said.

'Never mind that, matey. You get down to his office right away and ask him for the week off. The mood he's in at the moment, he'll probably give you a pay rise as well.'

'We'll see,' I said, turning to go.

'Oh, Richard,' Philip called, just as I was about to close the door behind me.

'Yes.'

'Is it true Charlotte's going to be a waitress at this solicitors' do?'

'Er . . .'

'I knew it,' he laughed, almost jumping up and down with glee, 'you haven't told her, have you?'

'Oh, yes I have.'

'You mean she agreed?'

'Not exactly.'

'Well, what *was* her reaction?'

'Difficult to know how to describe it, but I suppose it would have registered several points on the Richter Scale.'

'That's my girl!' Philip said, rubbing his hands together. 'Twenty pounds says she doesn't do it.'

'You're on,' I said defiantly.

'Like taking candy from a baby,' he said, shaking his head. 'Candy from a baby.'

I couldn't believe I'd said it. It was just foolish pride. To have bet twenty pounds on something as unlikely as Charlotte Morrison putting on a white apron and waiting at table was insane. As if it wasn't bad enough to lose my secretary. Now I was due to lose twenty quid as well.

The weight of these matters was bearing down on me so heavily that I almost walked into the Chairman before I saw him.

'Deep in thought, Richard?'

'Oh, hello, Bob. I was on my way to see you.'

'Why, what's the problem?'

'No problem, really. I just wondered if I could take next week off.'

'Fine as far as I'm concerned. What are you planning?'

I explained about the proposed holiday.

'Excellent,' he said. 'I'm sure you'll enjoy it. Just make

sure that you come back in one piece. I don't want any
drop-outs for this lunch. By the way, have you told
Charlotte about it?'

'Well . . . yes . . . and . . . er . . .'

'Good! Good! Well. I must get my skates on. If I don't
see you before you go, have a good holiday.'

'Er . . . thanks,' I said, as he strode off.

I meandered slowly back to my office. My twenty
pounds was as good as lost.

Chapter 16

'You didn't mention we'd be sharing a room,' Philip complained, dropping his suitcase noisily onto the floor next to his narrow bed.

'I wasn't sure we would be,' I said, stretching out on my own bed to the accompaniment of several loudly twanging springs.

'I'd assumed you'd be shacked up with Miss Bishop,' Philip went on, gently lowering himself onto his duvet.

'After one dinner date?'

'No point letting the grass grow under your feet,' he went on, lying back and gazing at the ceiling. 'I must say, she is rather nice. How come she's not attached?'

'Broke up with her boyfriend four months ago and still recovering from the trauma.'

'Oh, no, I can't bear it!' he groaned, burying his head under his pillow for a moment. 'You're both in the same boat – emotional cripples. It's the blind leading the partially sighted.'

'And what about you?' I asked. 'Are you trying to tell me that your divorce has left you unscarred?'

'Water under the bridge, dear boy, as Patrick Faulkner would say. No, as far as I'm concerned there's no point moping around. The world's my oyster. And talking of pearls – what do you know about Caroline?'

'Not a lot. She's a friend of Sarah's; she's something in advertising, and she can't ski.'

'Oh, good! That means she'll be in beginners' class with us.'

'Yes,' I said, 'it seems there's just the three of us who haven't skied before. All the others looked rather professional.'

Philip and I had definitely felt inferior on being introduced to the other members of the group at Gatwick. To begin with, everybody else – all eight of them – looked a good deal fitter and better prepared for the piste than we did. What was more, several of them were bristling with skis and ski sticks and talking incomprehensibly about being up to their waists in light powder, wiping out on the Hahnenkamm, and hitting the mogul fields in the Trois Vallées.

'Any idea what they're talking about?' Philip had asked.

'None,' I'd replied.

The seating on the aircraft had been well spread out, so we hadn't had a lot of opportunity to get to know each other. Much the same thing had happened on the coach from Geneva to Courmayeur, our chosen resort. As a result, by the time we passed through the Mont Blanc tunnel into Italy, Philip and I were still as much in the dark about the whole business as we had been at the outset.

'I didn't really get a chance to talk to any of them, did you?' he asked.

'No, we'll just have to find out who they all are at dinner tonight.'

Before Philip could reply there was a knock at our door. 'Wake up, you two,' Sarah called. 'It's time to get organised.'

'Okay, we're coming,' I said, dragging myself from my bed.

'Here we go,' Philip groaned. 'The ordeal begins.'

And how right he was. Our arrival in the town had been too late in the afternoon to do any skiing, but it was agreed that we should all get our lift passes, and those of us who needed to hire equipment could do that as well. We were duly frog-marched through the cobbled streets by James, one of the members of our party who knew about this sort of thing, eventually arriving at some sort of ski centre.

The place was heaving with a dozen different nationalities all shouting at the tops of their voices. Above it all, every now and then, an hysterical Italian voice would shriek out, only to be lost again in the general hubbub. The whole place seemed to be a lesson in anarchy.

'I'll say one thing for the Italians,' Philip remarked as he elbowed his way through the door, 'they don't allow their lives to be blighted by unnecessary regimentation.'

'Now,' James bellowed, 'the first thing we have to do is get our photos taken for the ski passes. The photo booth is over there . . . ' he pointed to the far corner of the room, ' . . . let's go for it!'

And go for it we did. With all the finessse of a rugby scrum we powered our way through the throng, reaching our goal surprisingly quickly despite concerted international resistance.

'That was amazing,' Sarah commented. 'I think, between the door and here, I was insulted in every Western European language there is.'

'I don't remember hearing Dutch,' I said.

'Oh, yes,' James replied, 'I received a heavy burst of Dutch very early on. No Norwegian though.'

'No,' Philip agreed. 'But I'm sure I took a light peppering of Swedish somewhere there in the middle.'

Some considerable time later, but now with our ski passes hanging about our necks, we made our slightly more orderly way to the equipment hire area. It was only more orderly because access was through a narrow doorway and down a corridor. I have no doubt that without that natural filter, two hundred people would have exploded into the fitting area at once and crushed the attendants to death.

I placed my right foot on the low bench in front of a particularly laidback individual who seemed to be in charge of boot hire. He gazed down at my size ten and a half with an expression which combined disbelief and scientific interest. Then he shook his head.

'No possibal!' he said, throwing his hands up as a sign of hopelessness.

'What?' I asked.

'No possibal!' he repeated, shaking his head again and laughing a short, irritating sort of laugh. 'No possibal!'

'What . . . is . . . no . . . possibal?' I asked, slowly and loudly, just in case he didn't speak English.

He laughed again and pointed to my foot. Then he made that two-handed gesture chiefly used by fishermen indicting the dimensions of the one that got away. 'No possibal!' he repeated, once more.

'He seems to be admitting defeat when it comes to finding you a pair of boots, old lad,' Philip remarked.

'So it would seem,' I said. 'But he's just going to have to try harder, I'm afraid.'

After much prompting; several searches on his part; several rejections on mine; another search and a sharp exchange of views with an impatient group of Germans behind me; I eventually settled for a pair of boots probably only half a size too small. I hobbled over to the racks of skis.

'Ask for short skis,' Sarah advised. 'They're much easier to control when you're starting out.'

'Okay.'

'Short! Short!' I said to the tanned moustachioed figure responsible for equipping me. As I spoke I indicated the skis should come no higher than my navel.

He eyed me up and down critically, turned to the rack behind him and produced a pair of skis approximately seven feet long.

'No, no,' Sarah cut in. 'Short! Short!'

There followed a general, full and frank discussion regarding the optimum length of skis for a six foot two inch novice. Whether any of us knew what the others were saying I'm not sure, since we all confined ourselves to our native tongues – including the bunch of Germans who had by that time caught up with us again. In the end, a compromise was arrived at and I was issued with skis that just about reached my nose.

Finally, complete with pass, boots, skis and sticks, I fought my way back through the steaming throng and out into the cold, clean, late afternoon air. I stood there and breathed deeply a couple of times while Philip, Sarah and Caroline popped out, one by one, into the street.

'Well, that was exciting,' Philip said. 'I'm exhausted and I haven't even set foot on the slopes yet.'

According to the brochure, if you picked the right time, there was little queuing for the cable car which carried you from the town up into the mountains. It was evident the next morning that the right time was not eight o'clock. The scrummage of humanity twisted in a long, disorderly, winding mass around the metal barriers inside the cable car station, down the long steps and into the road.

'Whose bright idea was it to get up at seven o'clock so we could queue here until nine?' Caroline muttered behind me.

'We've got to get there early to enrol for ski school,' James explained patiently from somewhere even further back in the line.

'Do you reckon this ski school business is essential?' Philip asked, quietly. 'I mean, couldn't we just have a crack at it on our own?'

'I've no idea,' I said, picking up my skis and sticks as the next surge forward promised to take place. 'Since we haven't put these things on yet, it's hard to judge.'

'I suppose you're right,' he said, as we were suddenly

taken up and swept along like pebbles on a beach. 'We can always see how it goes this morning.'

Half an hour later, laden with nearly one hundred and fifty souls, the cable car swung out across the valley and began its ascent to Plan Checrouit and the nursery slopes.

'Blimey!' Philip said, twisting round in the crush and rubbing at the misted glass with his sleeve, 'look at that view.'

I gazed out as the great south face of Mont Blanc loomed high in the distance.

'Breathtaking stuff,' I remarked.

'So's this,' added my colleague, taking a swig from a silver hip flask which had magically appeared from somewhere inside his ski suit. 'Have a slug,' he said, handing it to me. 'Guaranteed twelve-year-old malt.'

With some difficulty, due to the cramped conditions, I took the flask from him and had a swig. Instantly, I was ready for the slopes.

'Okay – everybody, your skis on, plees,' Danielle instructed with a disarming smile.

She was dark, pretty, petite and very French. There had been four beginnners' classes, but Philip and I had made sure that we, along with Caroline, got in Danielle's. Apart from anything else, she looked as though she had a sense of humour, and we felt that anybody teaching us would need a sense of humour.

'Today I weel teech you 'ow to snewplough and 'ow to tern.'

'Oh, goody!' Philip said. 'I've always wanted to know 'ow to snewplough and 'ow to . . .'

We were standing on the gentlest of inclines. Allowing for that, and the fact that Philip was a complete novice, and that he was travelling backwards, the speed he managed to achieve, over the relatively short distance he traversed before crashing to the ground, was really quite remarkable.

'Pheeleep!' Where are you going?'

'Nowhere any more,' he said, struggling to get up, 'but I seemed to be heading back towards Courmayeur for a while then.'

As he spoke he managed to haul himself up to a point where he looked like a cross between Bambi and one of those pieces of modern sculpture made out of odds and ends and scrap metal. His legs had got crossed at some stage, and despite his best efforts his skis were very slowly travelling in opposite directions. Most of his weight was consequently being supported by his ski sticks which were getting further and further away from his skis. Eventually, once again, and this time with a faint, despairing cry which failed to do justice to his near superhuman struggle, he crumpled to the ground.

'I hope he's not hurt,' Caroline said, as Danielle skied across to untangle him.

'He'll be all right as long as he hasn't fallen on his hip flask,' I replied.

The snowplough is the most elementary of skiing techniques. You stand, feet apart, with the tips of your skis almost touching in front of you in a big V-shape. In this position, with the inside edge of each ski biting into the snow, one should be able to ski down any piste just as slowly as one wants. A slight redistribution of weight from one ski to the other will produce a correspondingly opposite change in direction. At least, that was what happened when Danielle did it. Somehow it wasn't quite the same when the class attempted it.

One by one they teetered, slithered, pirouetted and tumbled. It was pathetic, and just made me even more determined to succeed.

'Okay, Reechard – GO!'

It was my turn. I took off. Slowly, very slowly, I set off down the nursery slope, my legs locked rigidly in the snowplough position. A little more weight on the right

237

ski . . . a little turn to the left . . . a little more weight on the left ski . . . a little turn to the right . . . It was working! It was working! It was easy after all. But if it was *easy* why was I drenched in perspiration? Never mind! Concentrate! Concentrate! A little more weight on the right ski . . . a little turn to the left . . . a little more weight on the left ski . . . a little turn to the right . . . a bit too much weight on the right ski . . . a great big turn to the left . . . all my weight on the left ski . . . why was I pointing uphill?

As a result of a fairly complicated manoeuvre which involved my travelling in reverse for a short distance I found myself pointing downhill again but, alas, the snowplough position was lost. With skis very nearly parallel I hurtled off in the general direction of Danielle, who was wisely waiting further down the slope at what she judged to be a safe distance.

For some reason the novice skier tends to lean backwards when out of control. I suppose it's because if you do that when you're walking or running, you will either fall over or just stop anyway. Unfortunately, the result is quite different when you are on skis. The more I leant back, the more the tips of my skis lifted and the faster I went. All steering gone, I flashed past Danielle at what felt like the speed of light.

'Snewplough! Snewplough!' she wailed.

I suppose it must have happened to lots of other people, otherwise they wouldn't have put all that safety netting there in the first place. As I lay on my back, covered in snow and hopelessly ensnared, I tried to remove the encrusted ice from my sunglasses. A swish of skis heralded Danielle's arrival.

'That was very spectacular, Reechard,' she laughed, 'but it was not a snewplough.'

Replacing my sunglasses and staggering to my feet, I became aware of a maniacal shriek coming from further up the slope. I shaded my eyes and looked. It was

Philip. He seemed to be finding my performance amusing.

'You now!' Danielle shouted, waving a ski stick to signal him to begin.

He started out quite well, then, just like the rest of us, it all went wrong. It looked as though his ski tips might have crossed. Whatever it was that happened, he veered to the right suddenly, then violently to the left. After that he just went straight downhill.

Like me, in his panic he just leant back further and further. As a result he hurried off down the piste in an almost perfect sitting position.

'Look at 'im – 'e is on the lavatory,' Danielle said disparagingly. 'All you Engleesh, you ski like you are always on the lavatory!'

With these few words of encouragement she set off after my comrade, who, remarkably, was still gathering speed.

Set at a considerable distance from our nursery slopes, was a big, open, wooden building. It seemed to provide some sort of garaging for the piste-bashers – the huge caterpillar-tracked vehicles that knock the pistes back into shape at the end of a hard day's skiing. Just outside the building, in splendid isolation, stood a large, galvanised steel bin. What it was for I have no idea, but it must have been almost seven feet high and four or five feet in diameter. Watching Philip, his arms flailing as he continued to career downhill, it struck me momentarily that he was heading in the general direction of this small, built-up area.

Naturally, it gave me no cause for concern. The distance he would have to cover would be far too great and he was obviously bound to fall at any moment. And yet, somehow he was managing to stay upright, and every time he veered away from the most direct route to that building, he was drawn back to it again as if by some sort of magnetic force-field.

239

Now everbody on the slope seemed mesmerised by his progress. They couldn't take their eyes off him. But deep down we all knew he'd be all right. He'd never reach the building. He couldn't possibly ski that distance. No, he wouldn't ski into the only structure for miles around and actually hurt himself.

The sonorous clang of the galvanised steel bin when he hit it echoed up and down the Aosta valley like some mournful temple gong. As its reverberations died away everything around was silent. The static audience peered down at the tiny, prone figure. Then there was a familiar shriek of laughter from down below and I knew Hampson's still had a silver specialist.

'I think I'm going to head back to the hotel,' Caroline said, as we finished our lunch. 'I'm absolutely exhausted.'

'Oh, that's a shame,' Philip replied. 'Are you sure?'

'Yes,' she smiled, 'I'm going to have a long, hot bath and a sleep. I'll see you at dinner. And don't hurt yourselves. You two are lethal.'

Philip watched admiringly as she made her way out of the restaurant. 'Nice girl,' he said. 'I think she was really concerned about us.'

'Philip,' I replied, 'everybody in the class was really concerned about us.'

'Yes,' he said, emptying his glass. 'Okay! What are we going to do this afternoon? Practice more snowploughs and turns so we can impress Danielle tomorrow morning?'

'All right, but let's go on one of those tows first.'

'Good idea. We can master the technique of using those things before Danielle demonstrates it tomorrow. That should impress her.'

For lunch, we had retreated, battered and bruised, to the village of Dolonne at the foot of the cable car. Despite being both physically and mentally shattered, Philip and I, unlike Caroline, had been greatly restored

240

by lunch. This was probably due at least in part to the fact that, unlike Caroline, we had taken the opportunity to consume enough alcohol to deaden all pain – even that caused by ski boots half a size too small.

There was only one tow in Dolonne. It was very short and it served the gentle nursery slope there. We could see it from where we sat at the table. It was no more than a hundred yards away – down a little incline towards a frozen stream, across a narrow foot-bridge and up the other side.

The tow itself was of the button variety. It was basically a continually moving cable, hung at intervals with individual spring-loaded wires. On the end of each wire hung a metal disc, like a big button, about nine inches in diameter. The knack was to wait at the bottom of the slope, reach up and grab a disc as it passed by, and then put it between your legs as if you were going to sit on it. Once the wire had unwound to its full extent you would get pulled along, on your skis, up the hill. At the top you let go of the button and skied away as the thing automatically recoiled and headed off downhill again. It was easy. We'd watched people doing it that morning.

Outside the restaurant, Philip and I put on our skis again and turned towards the bridge.

'Okay, let's go!' I said.

'I'm right behind you,' he confirmed.

Why we hadn't noticed from the restaurant I don't know, but the path down to the bridge was really quite narrow, with snow banked up waist high on either side. This presented a problem since, to be effective, our very basic snowplough technique required wide open spaces. Indeed, that morning, the entire nursery slopes at Plan Checrouit had been insufficient to contain us, so this little path stood no chance at all.

Undeterred, I slithered towards the start of the track – a constricted opening between the two banks of snow.

241

My blood was awash with gluhwein and grappa. I knew no fear.

I missed the opening by about a foot, embedding my ski-tops in the snowdrift instead. My companion tried, but met with similar results. Suddenly, the hundred yards to the tow looked much, much further than it had from the restaurant.

Philip was the first to actually set a ski on the path. He let out a brief cry of triumph then he was gone: hurtling towards the narrow footbridge, bouncing off the snow walls like a ball in a pinball machine. I followed him almost immediately. Too close behind him to have noticed that the path was a sheet of ice, I rattled down through the little ravine, completely out of control. For a moment it looked as though Philip was actually going to shoot straight across the little bridge to the safety of the uphill section on the other side. It was just a shame that the handrails of the structure were so close together while his legs were so far apart.

As he went down, a sprawling mass of skis, gloves, sun glasses and the odd bit of woodwork from the bridge, I had to make a quick decision. I could either ski straight into him or miss the bridge completely and take my chance in the frozen stream. It was no contest: at least I'd stop if I hit him.

Unfortunately, my plan was foiled by one of his ski-sticks which he'd abandoned rather untidily in my path. Skiing over it, I was immediately and dramatically diverted to the left of the bridge. To my horror I catapulted off the path, dropping about a foot into the little gully where my skis became embedded in both banks, leaving me suspended in mid-air. I clutched frantically at the bridge handrail, then just stood there, bouncing up and down on my sagging skis, wondering what to do next.

It seemed to take us an inordinately long time to sort ourselves out. Philip was unable to unravel himself for

242

some minutes, and when he did eventually come to my assistance his first act was to howl with laughter. After a few sobering words from me, he clambered down into the gully where he was seized by a fresh attack of hysteria. It was almost fifteen minutes before we eventually hauled ourselves up the slippery path to the plateau on the other side of the bridge.

We had been concentrating so single-mindedly on getting out of the gully, repairing the bridge and just staying upright that we'd quite forgotten that the whole performance was easily visible from the restaurant where we'd had lunch. As we crested the brow of the hill there was an explosion of applause, cheering and laughter. Looking up, we were confronted with a packed terrace of beautiful people swathed in furs, sunglasses and smiles. I would judge that ninety per cent of them were Italian. Probably a similar proportion never actually put on skis. And why should they? They were there to look good, not to get covered in snow.

One tall, immaculate, grey-haired gentleman at the front, bottle in one hand, glass in the other, led the assembled party in a toast to our determination or, possibly, just our entertainment value – it was difficult to tell which from where we were standing.

Not to be outdone, Philip produced his hipflask and we returned the compliment to another round of applause.

'When did you do this?' I asked, inspecting a sizeable dent which now disfigured the vessel.

'When I skied into that bloody great cast-iron dustbin this morning,' he said, looking ruefully at the flask. 'Never mind, it still works all right.'

Against all the odds, not only did we eventually make it to the tow, we also went on to survive our first week's skiing. Although, as our confidence grew, so did our recklessness, thus ensuring that we were always dangerous to be near. The day after Danielle had

243

taught us that satisfying sideways, sliding stop that encrusts anybody within range in a jacket of snow and ice, I thundered down on my first lift queue of the day. At the last moment I slewed sideways and dug in the edges of my skis in the approved manner. It must have been a lot icier than I had imagined, or perhaps I just got it wrong, for rather than stopping I seemed to accelerate. Travelling sideways as I was, my skis had roughly the same effect on the queue as does a combine harvester on a field of ripe wheat. I only really recall the first person I hit. He was small, immaculately dressed in a pure white ski suit, and very, very Italian. I don't think he even saw my thirteen stone coming, and I felt only the slightest impact as I passed over him and scythed my way through the rest of the queue. It took some time to prise him out of the ground, but fortunately he was too deeply in shock to complain much.

By the end of the week even the three of us who were novices were managing to get down most pistes, albeit with little style and lots of bruises. More importantly, we had acquired that second sense needed to always get back to the hotel in time to have a bath before the hot water ran out, and we'd also become fully conversant with Italian discotheque charges. We'd quickly learnt it wasn't the entrance fee or the price of the drinks you had to watch out for, it was what they charged for simply handing you back your coat at the end of the evening that could bankrupt you.

It was a protracted negotiating session over that very matter on the last night that gave Sarah and me our first real moments alone during the whole week. Leaving the others to haggle, we escaped from the sticky heat of the disco into the sharp, crystal-clear alpine night. Arm in arm we strolled back through the old streets to the hotel.

'I hope you've enjoyed it,' Sarah said. 'It was a bit unfair of me to subject you to a whole crowd of people you didn't know.'

'Not at all – it's been fun. I'm covered in bruises; I think I've sprained my knee; my feet are probably permanently damaged; and I'm quite sure I've got alcoholic sclerosis of the liver. No, I've enjoyed it immensely.'

'Oh, good,' she laughed, 'as long as you've got no complaints.'

'I didn't say that.'

'You mean you have?'

'Yes – I haven't seen anything of you.'

'Only every day . . .'

'You know what I mean.'

'Well, it's not easy to be intimate in a party of ten.'

'I know,' I said. 'It's just that I thought I felt a little coolness on your part from the moment we met up at Gatwick. Was I imagining it?'

She stopped and looked at me. 'Probably not,' she said. 'Most people in the group knew Peter, my ex . . .'

'I know,' I said. 'And you found that difficult?'

'Yes, I felt they were weighing you up to see if you were a suitable replacement.'

'Understandable.'

'Perhaps, but I still found it annoying. I'd rather make up my own mind about my relationships, and the truth is . . .' she paused, ' . . . the truth is, Richard, I don't really know what I do want at the moment.'

'The truth is, Sarah, neither of us really knows what we want at the moment.'

She laughed again. 'Does that make us compatible, do you think?'

'It has been suggested it's a case of the blind leading the partially sighted.'

'Sounds like pure Philip Lawrence.'

'Who else?'

We continued our stroll, still arm in arm, in silence for a while. As the hotel came into sight, Sarah was the first to speak.

'I do like you, Richard,' she said.

'Me too.'

'I'm being serious.'

'Me too.'

'Richard!'

'Well, spit it out – say what you want to say.'

'All right. I really do like you . . . it's just that . . . just that . . .'

'You're not absolutely sure, and you don't want to get hurt again?'

'Yes,' she sighed.

'So, what's the problem?'

'Well, I don't know what you're expecting from me . . .'

'Oh, sex, sin, passion. You know – all the usual stuff.'

A well-aimed punch landed in my already bruised rib-cage. 'You're not taking me seriously,' she complained. 'I don't find it easy to talk about this sort of thing . . .'

'Then let's just take one step at a time,' I suggested. 'If it works out, all well and good. If it doesn't – that's life. At least we'll both have gone into it with our eyes open.'

'You'll have to be incredibly patient with me.'

'I will.'

'And not try to rush me.'

'I won't.'

'Do you promise?'

'I do.'

'Good,' she said, as we entered the darkened, creaky little hotel foyer.

'And now,' I whispered in the darkness, 'at the risk of rushing things – do I get a goodnight kiss?'

'Yes,' she said, sliding her arms around behind my neck, 'I think you probably do.'

A moment later the street door burst open, there was a brief waft of alcohol and somebody or something crashed into us.

'Bloody hell! Who's that?' said a familiar, loud voice.

'It's us, Philip. For goodness' sake keep your voice down.'

'Who'sh ush?' Caroline slurred from somewhere nearby in the darkness.

'Richard and Sarah, of course, you pair of drunken lunatics,' I whispered.

'What d'you mean – drunk?' Philip said, dropping his voice to a hoarse whisper. 'We're not drunk.'

'Then why did you come through that door like Genghis Khan's vanguard,' Sarah hissed.

'Cos,' Caroline began, 'we were being chashed by people from the disco, because . . .'

'No, Caroline,' I protested, 'don't tell us. Please don't tell us. Let's just go to bed before we wake up the whole hotel.'

'Good idea,' Philip whispered, nudging me in the darkness. 'Fancy re-arranging bedrooms?'

'You're joking – she's plastered!'

'Who – Sarah? She's not, is she? She sounds all right to me.'

'No, you idiot – Caroline.'

'So I should hope,' he hissed, his voice now almost inaudible. 'She's cost me a fortune this evening – she's been soaking it up like a sponge for hours.'

'I feel sick . . . ' said a tiny voice.

'Not here!' Sarah ordered. 'Quick! Get to the bathroom.'

' . . . feel sick . . . ' Caroline confirmed.

'Hope she makes it,' Philip said, as Caroline was dragged, noisily up the stairs by her room-mate. 'What a terrible waste of alcohol.'

'Well, you know about the best laid plans . . .'

'Yes, yes,' he replied. 'But, I suppose we rather spoiled your plans as well?'

'What plans?'

'Oh, come on! Don't tell me you two were discussing alpine flowers when we arrived?'

'No.'

'Oh, just innocently kissing goodnight, perhaps?'

'Now, it's funny you should mention that,' I said.

'Oh, come on, Harton!' my companion said dismissively as he groped his way towards the staircase. 'Pull the other one – it's got sleigh-bells on!'

Chapter 17

'You didn't tell him, you . . . you . . . fink!'

'Fink? Fink? What exactly is a fink?' I asked, crossing the office to the bookcase.

'I don't know,' Charlotte snarled, 'but whatever it is, it's got to be better than you.'

'Ah, here it is,' I said, having thumbed through the rather tatty, office dictionary. 'According to this, it's a strike-breaker; an informer or a contemptible person – etymology unknown.'

'Well, that just about sums you up.'

'What – etymology unknown?'

'No – contemptible person. I mean, how could you do it, Richard?'

'Easy – I just kept my big mouth shut for once.'

'But you said . . .'

'I said, I would handle it my way.'

'But you haven't done anything!'

'That was my way of handling it.'

'Ho, ho! Very clever!'

'I thought so.'

'Oh, it's pointless talking to you!'

'About this particular matter – yes, it is.'

'Great! So you're just going to do nothing.'

'That's right.'

'Why?' she shouted.

'Because, Charlotte, there is nothing I can do. You and Bob Derby have elected to fight a battle about this.

You're both in your trenches, guns aimed and ready to fire, and if you think I'm going to start wandering about in no-man's land, you can forget it. I'd simply get shot – probably by both of you.'

'So, you're just going to let me walk out – just like that?'

'I don't want you to leave,' I said, 'but between the two of you, you've reached an impasse. If you don't do this wretched waitressing job, Bob will go berserk; and according to you, you'll leave rather than do it, anyway. It's impossible. Unless . . .'

Charlotte looked up from her desk, where she'd been sitting, head in hands. 'Unless what?' she asked suspiciously.

'Unless, just this once, you're prepared to swallow your pride and . . .'

'No!'

' . . . and take a little cash bonus from me as a personal token of how much I appreciate your sacrifice.'

'How much?' she asked, even more suspiciously.

'Twenty pounds.'

'Twenty pounds?' She hesitated, ' . . . no . . . no, I mean, this is a matter of principal . . .'

'I know, but principal won't pay the rent when you're fired.'

'I know that,' she said, apparently beginning to give my proposition some thought. 'And *you'd* pay me? It wouldn't come from Hampson's?'

'No, it would come straight out of my pocket – a personal thank you for staying on. I really don't want you to leave, Charlotte. You may not be irreplacable, but you're the next best thing to it.'

'Twenty pounds, you say?'

'Yes. It's not a bad bonus for about an hour's work. But, if you really feel you can't . . .'

'I'll think about it,' she said.

250

'Good. I've got to go to Bailey's now and take their sale. Give it some thought while I'm out.'

'All right,' she said, 'but I'm not promising anything.'

I drove to Twickenham with a light heart: I'd produced a diplomatic solution to a dispute which had promised to degenerate into bloody, hand to hand combat; I'd effectively won my bet with Philip, and in doing so, conjured up a twenty pound bonus for Charlotte which was costing me nothing but which she thought was coming straight out of my own pocket. For once, all the pieces of the jigsaw had dropped neatly into place and I was going to get all the Brownie points.

Bailey's saleroom was a good place to go when one was floating along on a pink, cottonwool cloud of self-congratulatory euphoria. There was something so dog-eared and disreputable about the place that, as soon as I stepped through the door, my little cloud condensed and I crashed back into the real world.

'Hello, Mr H,' Harry Sutton said, brightly. Then he gripped me by the arm and lowered his voice to a more conspiratorial tone: 'Can I have a word, Sir? Nothing serious – just a word.'

'Of course, Harry,' I said. 'Is there a problem?'

'Well, not really, sir. Not really. It's just . . .' he drew close, glancing this way and that, 'it's just Peter McCallum . . .'

'Yes?'

'Well, he's . . . you know . . . he's . . . ' Harry nodded and winked furiously.

'He's what?'

'He's . . . well . . . he's . . . he's a bit . . . you know.'

I stared at him blankly and shook my head.

'You know!' he insisted, this time acting out the draining of a glass.

'You mean he's drunk?'

'Cor, blow me, sir!' Harry protested, once again looking over first one shoulder then the other before he

251

went on. 'No, I wouldn't say drunk, Sir. No, just a bit . . . you know . . .'

During my first week at Hampson's, Bob Derby had cautioned me about Peter McCallum's periodic binges. However, since the man had never been anything less than courteous, entertaining and sober in my presence, I'd forgotten all about it. Now it seemed I was about to meet the other Peter McCallum, and since Harry Sutton had judged it prudent to forewarn me, I couldn't help but feel that he was going to be a real Mr Hyde.

'Where is he?' I asked.

'Down the pub, Mr H.'

'At a quarter past ten in the morning?'

'It may be a quarter past ten in the morning to you and me, Mr H, but I reckon it's probably still last night to Peter.'

'You mean he hasn't been to bed?'

'Not if he's running true to usual form, Sir.'

'Oh, well,' I sighed, 'I suppose if he's not here he can't make a nuisance of himself.'

'No, there is that, Mr H,' Harry agreed, 'but I thought I'd better tip you the wink just in case he does turn up.'

'Do you think it's likely?'

'Just depends,' he said, shaking his head. 'He might drink till he drops – he does sometimes. On the other hand he might roll in here for his usual bit of the sale.'

Peter McCallums's 'usual bit of the sale' was the carpets and rugs section. Sometimes this would amount to little more than a few threadbare examples of Axminster and Wilton, but on other occasions there could be quite a varied selection.

That particular morning, there were just over eighty lots including some modern bankruptcy stock, a dozen or so quite nice old rugs, and about thirty modern ones consigned by a dealer who imported direct from the Middle East. It was a mixed bag but there was enough of interest to ensure a reasonable attendance by the rug-dealing fraternity.

It was shortly after half-past twelve that I finished selling the furniture. There was still no sign of Peter McCallum.

'That brings us to the carpets and rugs,' I said, looking over to Harry Sutton who had just taken up McCallum's normal position next to the large pile of rugs to the left of the rostrum. 'All set, Harry?'

'Yes, sir,' he confirmed. 'Ready when you are.'

Harry's task was to hold up each rug as it came up for sale, finally rolling it up quickly and stacking it away to one side.

'We start with Lot 240,' I announced. 'A quantity of celadon-green Wilton, cut and fitted. What will you bid me? Twenty pounds somewhere? Ten then? Ten I'm bid,' I said, pointing to a non-existent bidder in the middle of the room. I looked around to see if anyone was really interested. 'At ten pounds, then . . . ' I went on, ' . . . selling at ten pounds . . .'

A well dressed lady in the second row who had been fidgeting nervously throughout the last few lots of furniture suddenly thrust her catalogue high into the air.

'Twelve pounds . . . ' I said, ' . . . any advance on twelve . . . ?'

Once again she waved her catalogue high above her head.

'It is your bid at twelve pounds, madam,' I assured her. 'All done at twelve, then . . . ' I brought my hammer down sharply on the rostrum. 'Twelve pounds,' I confirmed. 'And the name is . . . ?'

The buyer, clearly an inexperienced auction-goer, stuttered out her name, blushed and sat back in her chair trying to compose herself. She had no need to worry: she'd got a bargain. There had been at least one other person in the room who'd looked as though he was going to bid, but I always liked to sell the odd probate lot cheaply. It tended to wake people up. The man in question would certainly be much faster with his next bid anyway.

'Lot 241,' I went on. 'A similar, smaller quantity of Wilton . . . bid me ten pounds again . . .'

This time half a dozen hands and catalogues shot into the air.

'Ten . . . twelve . . . fifteen . . . eighteen . . .' I called out before the would-be buyers could get their hands back down again, ' . . . at eighteen pounds, then . . .' I repeated, pointing at the scowling secondhand dealer who'd missed the first lot and was now in danger of buying the second at eight pounds more than he'd bid, ' . . . all done at eighteen . . .?' Down came the hammer again. There was something deeply satisfying about selling at Bailey's!

All continued to go well for another eleven lots. This took us up to the first of the rugs in Harry Sutton's pile.

'Lot 253,' I read from my auctioneer's book. 'An Afghan rug with lozenge border. Bid me . . .'

There was a sudden commotion amidst the group of dealers crowding around the rug pile and Peter McCallum burst onto the scene.

Peter was an Ulsterman. He was in his mid to late fifties, slightly built and always smart. His wavy, dark hair was normally slicked back and I'd never seen him without a tie. It was definitely his Mr Hyde alter ego who stood before me now. A wayward lock of hair hung down between his bright red eyes. His face was flushed and his shirt was open at the neck. Peter McCallum was a mess.

'Shorry I'm late, sir,' he mumbled, looking up at me through eyes that had suddenly become mere slits.

I nodded. I'd got two choices: to order him out of the gallery now, or to let him try and do his job. I had no doubt the former course would result in a very nasty scene. Far better to take the latter and see what happened.

I beckoned to Harry Sutton who crossed over to the

254

rostrum. 'I'll give him a chance,' I whispered, 'but, if he gets out of hand, he'll have to go – preferably without a fight.'

'Understood, sir,' Harry confirmed, looking distinctly nervous.

He went to return to where he'd been standing next to the rug pile, but McCallum waved him away. 'Smy job,' he declared, swaying a little, 'Shmy job!'

Harry looked up at me for guidance. I signalled him to remain where he was, next to the rostrum.

'Right, let's get on,' I said, 'Lot 253 . . . bid me fifty pounds . . .'

Much to my relief the next few lots sold without Peter McCallum falling over, starting a fight or being sick. In fact, the first problem I encountered was a frequent complaint from the floor.

'I can't see!' said a middle-aged upper-crust lady in the third row.

I could well believe it. The rug dealers had, as usual, spilled around the front of the rug pile so that they now very nearly encircled it. *I* could hardly see what was being shown, so I wasn't at all surprised to hear that nobody else could.

'Could you please move away to the side of the pile, gentlemen,' I asked.

A general shuffling and muttering took place which seemed to bring about no obvious improvement.

'Come along, gentlemen!' I said sharply. 'Get over to the side. Nobody can see what's going on.'

This time they started to move away as requested. Unfortunately, they didn't do so quite fast enough for Peter McCallum.

'Get back there! Go on! Get back there! Do what the auctioneer tellsh you, will you!' he demanded, pushing several of the offenders to one side.

'Here, steady on, steady on . . . don't push . . . ' the dealers complained, as they were brutally corralled,

255

' . . . don't go mad, Pete . . . no need to get nasty . . .
we're your bread and butter, remember . . .'

'Thank you, Peter,' I said, 'that's fine.'

'Get back there! Get back!' McCallum continued,
warming to his task.

'Peter!'

'Yesh, sir,' he said, apparently noticing me for the
first time for a while.

'That will do. Let's get on.'

'Whatever you say, sir.'

'Good . . . Lot 258 . . . a Shirvan rug . . . bid me . . . ' I
glanced to my left at the rug in question. Unfortunately,
what I saw was not a Shirvan but a modern Pakistan
Bokhara-patterned example instead.

'You're showing the wrong lot, Peter,' I pointed out.

Peter McCallum continued gazing into the middle
distance.

'You are showing the wrong lot,' I repeated. 'It
should be Lot 258 – the Shirvan.'

He looked at me vacantly, half smiling. 'What's that
you're saying, sir?'

'You are showing the wrong lot! It should be Lot
2-5-8!'

'That's what I'm showing,' he said, the smile fading.

'No, Pete, it's not,' said one of the dealers. 'It should
be a Shirvan . . . '

'Will you be minding your own business, mister!'

'Come on, Peter . . . ' Harry Sutton cut in.

'And you! I'm the carpets and rugs man! I know what
I'm doing! I'm not standing . . .'

'Peter!'

'Yesh, sir!'

'Come here!' I ordered.

'Yesh, sir!' He made his way over to the rostrum and
stood there, eyes almost closed, smiling up at me. 'What
is it I can do for you, sir?'

'You can either go home and sleep it off, or you can

stand here and keep quiet,' I whispered clearly and
distinctly to him. 'I don't mind which. Just stay away from
those rugs – Harry can show the rest.'

'But I . . . '

'But, nothing! You're drunk. Be quiet or get out.'

His watery eyes half-opened for a moment. Then he
opened his mouth, but no sound came out.

As Harry Sutton held up Lot 258 I re-started the sale:
'There we are now – the Shirvan . . . what will you bid
me? . . . a hundred and fifty? . . . one hundred I'm bid
. . . at one hundred and ten . . .'

For the next ten or twelve lots Peter McCallum
continued to loiter beside the rostrum, muttering to
himself the whole while. Although ninety per cent of
what he said was unintelligible, the remaining ten per
cent left it beyond doubt that it was a litany of contempt,
and that I had been singled out for special attention.
His recitation was eventually curtailed by the saleroom
telephone.

Mounted on the wall behind the rostrum, this
particular piece of telecommunications equipment was
a *bête noir* of mine. On sale days all calls were supposed
to be diverted to the office, except in the unlikely event
of someone wishing to bid over the telephone. Since, in
practice, telephone bids at Bailey's were slightly rarer
than Fabergé eggs, I could normally be certain that the
jangling bell behind me was simply confirmation that as
usual somebody had forgotten to divert the incoming
calls.

' . . . at eighty-five pounds . . . ' I said, swivelling in
the rostrum to glare at Harry for having failed yet again
to incapacitate the thing, ' . . . eighty-five pounds . . .
will somebody answer that phone!'

'I'll get it!' said a voice beside me, and before Harry
could drop the rug he was showing, Peter McCallum
had the telephone in his hand.

Harry Sutton looked helplessly from McCallum to me,

shrugged his shoulders, held Lot 270 high in front of him and effectively disappeared from sight.

'Yes, sir!' bellowed McCallum into the phone.

'Eighty-five . . . ninety . . . ninety-five . . . ' I said, scanning the room to see if rescue in any shape, size or form was at hand. The nearest thing to the US Cavalry that I could see was Polly Porter. He was studying his catalogue while leaning against a wardrobe at the back of the room and seemed happily unaware of our current crisis.

'Yessir!' boomed McCallum into the receiver again.

' . . . at ninety-five . . . one hundred . . . one hundred and ten . . . ' I continued, desperately trying to strike up some form of telepathic communication with Polly.

'Yes, sir . . . no sir . . . yes sir . . . ' Peter McCallum went on behind me.

' . . . one hundred and ten . . . are you all done at one hundred and ten? . . . selling then at one hundred and ten . . . ' At least I'd be able to summon Polly once I'd sold this lot. Although, even shouting at him promised to be a hit and miss affair since the expression of inner calm on his face confirmed beyond all doubt that he had switched off his hearing aid.

' . . . at one hundred and twenty . . . ' I said, noting a new bidder and cursing him, ' . . . one hundred and thirty . . . '

'Yessir . . . no sir . . . ' McCallum went on happily to the anonymous caller.

By now the only two people in the room paying any attention to me were the two bidders. Everyone else, with the exception of Polly Porter who was in his own little world anyway, was spellbound by the implausible telephone conversation going on behind me.

' . . . one hundred and forty . . . any more at one hundred and forty . . .?'

' . . . no sir . . . no sir . . . '

' . . . sold then, at one hundred and forty pounds,' I said, with ill-disguised relief, when I at last got the opportunity to bring down the hammer.

' . . . yes sir . . . yes sir . . .'

As I jotted down the details of the last sale in my book I glanced round at Peter – he was looking perplexed.

' . . . very shorry madam!' he said, and replaced the receiver.

As Peter McCallum wove his way across the room towards the door, Polly Porter grappled with the controls of his hearing aid. Something had brought the house down and he hadn't the faintest idea what it was. As for McCallum, he didn't look back. I'm not even sure he'd heard the laughter. His fuddled mind was on other things.

'McCallum was in a dreadful state,' I observed to Harry Sutton after the sale.

'He was, Mr H,' he agreed. 'I'm sorry, but we never get any warning when he's going on a bender. It's the first time for ages that he's been like that on a sale day.'

'Oh, well, we survived,' I said, 'but I don't give much for his life expectancy if he gets in that sort of state very often.'

'Don't you waste any time worrying about Mac, sir. He'll go to ground for a couple of days then he'll come back through that door as bright as a button like he hadn't been away. It's just the way he is.'

Of course, Harry Sutton was right. The following week Peter was his old self again, and once more in full control of both his faculties and Bailey's carpets and rugs.

'Hello there, Mr H,' he greeted me cheerily. 'Haven't seen you for a long time. Where have you been hiding yourself?'

Whether he really remembered nothing of the previous week's pantomime, or whether it was just a piece of selective amnesia, I don't know. Not that it really mattered. As Harry Sutton had said: it was just the way he was.

Chapter 18

'If you just feel the edge of the dish or the cover with your fingernail, you should be able to detect quite clearly that the silver overlaps the copper and creates a tiny ridge.'

A murmur of confirmation went round the assembled company of legal eagles as they passed the items around.

'This is because of the way in which Sheffield Plate was produced,' Philip went on, heroically simulating enthusiasm. 'A sheet of silver was laid on a sheet of copper and then the two were fused by being heated and passed between heavy rollers.'

Heads nodded in understanding.

'And since the silver was softer and more ductile than the copper, it overlapped, leaving this distinctive ridge. It's the easiest way of telling whether an item is Sheffield Plate or just electroplate.'

Bob Derby started to rise to his feet.

'And remember,' Philip continued undeterred, 'never, ever re-plate a piece of old Sheffield Plate no matter how much copper's showing through. If you do you'll destroy its value at a stroke.'

'Thank you, Philip,' said Hampson's Chairman. 'I'm sure that if any of you have any questions, Mr Lawrence will be happy to answer them over lunch.'

Philip nodded as a quiet ripple of polite applause ran around his small but select audience.

As Bob Derby led the party of solicitors out of the silver department and towards the lift, Philip Lawrence and I brought up the rear.

'Well done,' I said, 'you even had me convinced that you knew what you were talking about.'

'Pearls before swine,' he muttered. 'They're a pretty dry bunch. Lunch doesn't exactly promise to be a bundle of laughs.'

'All in the line of duty.'

'It's all right for you,' he went on, 'it's your office that's going to pick up the business from this little session. All I get is a load of extra work, an indifferent lunch *and* I end up twenty pounds down on the deal.'

'Ah, the evil of gambling!'

'Twenty pounds!' he repeated, as we waited for the party to wedge themselves into the lift.

'Philip and I will take the stairs,' I called to Bob Derby, who, despite being jammed at the back of the lift, was struggling to reach the control buttons just inside the door. 'We'll see you in the Boardroom.'

'Good idea,' he replied, as the doors slid closed. The lift shuddered once, then creaked off down to the ground floor.

'Twenty pounds!' Philip repeated again, as we ambled down the stairs. 'I mean, that's a lot of money – I can't afford to lose twenty quid.'

'Well, you know the old adage,' I said, 'never bet more than you can afford to lose.'

'No need to sound so pleased with yourself,' he snarled. 'Anyway, I could have sworn it was a dead cert.'

'I've never met a bankrupt gambler who didn't.'

'One more comment along those lines, Harton, and I swear I'll tip you over the bannisters.'

'No need to get nasty. I'd never imagined you as a bad loser.'

'I'm not,' he said. 'It's just that I still can't believe how wrong I was. I was absolutely certain that Charlotte

261

would have none of it. I really thought she'd give Hampson's two fingers before she'd be seen dishing out the meat and three veg.'

'Just goes to show how unpredictable people can be,' I said, as we arrived outside the Boardroom.

'No, no,' he said, shaking his head, 'no, she was nobbled somehow. You've promised her something.'

'Nonsense! It's nothing more than departmental loyalty – something you wouldn't understand of course.'

'Balls!' he replied, as he opened the door. 'After you, old chap.'

'No, no,' I insisted, 'after you, dear boy.'

Charlotte was standing just inside, next to the sideboard, helping to dispense drinks.

'Large gin and tonic and make it snappy, waitress,' Philip said, as soon as he saw her.

'Sod off!' she murmured, her face fixed in the most sickly of smiles.

'Tut! Tut! Tut!' he said, turning to me. 'It's just so difficult to get good domestic staff these days, don't you find?'

Charlotte's right foot lashed out suddenly, the toe of her shoe making good contact with my companion's left shin.

He winced. 'Okay, okay – I give in. I know when I'm beaten. Never let it be said that Philip Lawrence welshes on his gambling debts.' Then, before I could stop him, he'd produced two crisp, new ten-pound notes from his wallet. 'I think Charlie should have these really,' he went on, thrusting them into my hand, 'but I'll let you two fight that one out.' With that, he went to join the rest of the party at the far end of the room.

'G and T for me as well, please,' I said, as cheerfully as possible, hurriedly stuffing the money into my pocket.

'Gambling debts?' Charlotte said, sickly smile still firmly in place.

'Just one of Philip's little jokes,' I replied, managing

a nervous laugh.

'What was the bet about?' she asked, her cool, quiet tone contrasting threateningly with the mask-like countenance.

'Oh . . . nothing really . . .'

'It was about me, wasn't it?'

'You!' Another nervous laugh. 'Good Lord, no . . . no . . . not about you, Charlotte.'

'You had a bet on whether or not I'd do this job. Didn't you?' As she spoke, her eyes shone. Two and two had been put together and she'd come up with four.

I in turn calculated that it was no time for dithering denials. 'The money's yours anyway,' I said, hurriedly, picking up my drink.

'Which money's that, Richard? The money out of *your* own little pocket? The twenty pounds that *you* were going to pay me to show how much *you* appreciated my sacrifice?'

'We'll talk about this afterwards,' I said. 'I must join the others.'

'But, Richard,' she cooed, in a siren-like tone, 'you silly old thing, there's *nothing* to talk about.'

'What do you mean?' I asked, all alarm bells now ringing.

'What I say – there's nothing to talk about. Either you give me forty pounds or I'll wreck lunch.'

'Forty!'

'Forty.'

'Forget it.'

'Bye, bye, lunch.'

'Charlotte . . .'

'Are you ready to join us, Richard?' Bob Derby enquired.

'Yes, yes, I'm on my way, Bob,' I said, giving Charlotte a parting look which, although intended to be threatening, was probably redolent only of panic. That sickly sweet smile haunted me as I turned away to join

263

the party gathered around the large, circular, boardroom table. I had no way of telling what she was going to do, but I knew I had to expect the worst.

'So, how are you enjoying Hampson's, Mr Harton?' the solicitor on my left asked as we took our seats.

'Very challenging,' I said, trying hard to recall his name. 'Of course, I'm still settling in, but there's no doubt that the potential is massive,' I went on, wondering where exactly Charlotte was, and what she was doing.

'It must be very exciting.'

'Oh, it is,' I agreed. 'One's never quite sure what's going to happen next.'

'Water?' I heard Charlotte enquire, in a soft, honeyed tone which confirmed that the ghastly smile was still firmly in place.

'Yes, water anybody?' Bob Derby repeated. 'There will be wine of course.'

As he spoke, I felt the ice-cold liquid suddenly splash against the back of my neck.

'I'm so sorry, Mr Harton,' apologised the husky voice behind me. 'How clumsy of me.'

'Oh, don't mention it,' I said. 'It was nothing.'

'I think I'd like some,' said my nameless companion, rather rashly.

'Certainly, sir,' replied the smile behind me.

As my would-be assassin stepped up to fill his glass, I took the opportunity to lean forward in my chair to put myself out of range of any similar attacks of that type.

'Water for you, Mr Harton?' she asked.

'Er, no thank you,' I said. 'I think I've had enough already.'

Face still set in that awful television-advertisement-leer, she set off round the table to fill the other glasses.

'Pretty girl,' observed the man on my left.

'Yes,' I said, 'she's my secretary.'

'Lucky man,' he said, approvingly. 'She looks great fun.'

'Oh, laugh a minute,' I confirmed.

As far as I was concerned, this was not an atmosphere conducive to doing business. Although I tried to concentrate on promoting Hampson's in general and my department in particular, each time I heard a movement behind me I braced myself for a jug of water down the neck or a stiletto in the back. In the end, the attack, when it came, was full frontal.

'Excuse me, Mr Harton,' interrupted one of Charlotte's colleagues, as I was busy trying to look fascinated by the man on my right – this wasn't easy since he was in the middle of a particularly galling endorsement of the service provided by one of our rivals. 'Would you prefer to start with the paté or the lobster bisque?'

'Oh, the soup, please.'

'And for me,' said the man, temporarily halting his tribute to our competitors.

As the girl re-arranged our cutlery, it dawned on me that, under the circumstances, my choice of starter was tactically unsound. I had no doubt that Charlotte could do far more damage with a serving of lobster bisque than she might ever achieve with a little coarse paté and dry toast.

Undeterred by my fast glazing expression, the man on my right droned on happily as the soup plates were placed before us. Then, a moment later, a tureen arrived on the table between us. It was placed there by Charlotte Morrison.

Carefully, she ladled the soup into our guest's plate, then she turned to me. I looked straight ahead. Eye contact did not seem a good idea.

'Your soup, Mr Harton,' she said, carefully catching the ladle on the side of my plate and depositing the extremely hot contents straight into my lap. 'Oh, how *clumsy* of me! I'm so sorry! You *must* let me sponge you off!'

'No, no, really, please don't trouble yourself . . .'

'No, I *insist*. You *must* come through to the kitchen . . .'

She didn't actually add, 'or I'll tip the rest of the tureen straight over you while you sit there,' but I sensed that the threat was implied.

'Well, perhaps you're right,' I conceded.

'Oh, I am, I am,' she smiled.

I made my apologies to the assembled company and disappeared into the kitchen where, moments later I was joined by Charlotte. A manic light of triumph now gleamed in her eyes.

'Have you gone mad?' I snapped, on the basis that attack is generally the best form of defence.

'Never been more sane in my life, you cheap-skate. Forty pounds or Derby gets it.'

'What?'

'Forty pounds or Derby gets the iced water, or the custard, or just whatever I happen to decide on at the time.'

'Don't be ridiculous, Charlotte. This charade has gone on quite long enough.'

'I mean it, Richard,' she said, 'forty pounds or else!'

There was something about the way she said it. She really did seem to mean it.

'Thirty,' I said, sponging away at my trousers.

'Forty!'

'Thirty!' I insisted. Charlotte wasn't the only one who could be bloody-minded.

'The price is forty,' she said, turning to go back to the Boardroom. 'Let me know when you agree – but don't leave it too long. It's already later than you think.'

I finished cleaning the lobster bisque out of my trousers as best I could and returned to the Boardroom where the first course was being cleared away.

'All cleaned up?' asked the nameless solicitor on my left.

'Yes, thanks.'

266

'It was absolutely delicious,' he added, 'but I don't suppose you got a chance to discover that.'

'No, I said, 'all I know is that it was hot.'

The main course passed off without incident, but that just served to make me more, rather than less, nervous. It wasn't in Charlotte's nature to back down without a fight. The question was, when would she strike?

The answer came suddenly. I was deep in conversation across the table with the only guest whose name I could remember when I saw Charlotte appear abruptly behind Bob Derby's chair. She was armed with a jug full of iced water. I wasn't totally convinced she would go through with it, but she was wearing that awful smile again. All things considered, it didn't seem the right moment to test her resolve to destruction.

'May I have some water, please, Charlotte.'

'Of course, Mr Harton,' she said, coming round to where I was seated. 'Is it a deal?' she whispered, as she filled my glass.

'It's a deal,' I replied, 'forty pounds.'

'It's been a pleasure doing business with you,' she murmured, then melted away out of the room.

'She really is a jolly attractive girl that secretary of yours,' the man on my left said, 'but I bet she's a real handful.'

'Why do you say that?'

'Well, you know, all that red hair. She looks as though she could be an absolute firecracker – dangerous to handle once her fuse has been lit.'

'Oh, not really. It's just important that there's no doubt about who's the boss.

'Well, I'm very impressed,' he concluded. 'We don't seem to get girls like that queuing up to work at our offices. You auctioneers must pay your secretarial staff much more than we humble solicitors can afford.'

'Well,' I said, 'they certainly don't come cheap.'

Chapter 19

Charles Morrison-Whyte put down his cigar and took up his thick, morocco-bound diary.

'The last Saturday in the month, you say?'

'Yes,' I replied.

'Sorry, out of the question,' he said, after a moment's scrutiny. 'I'm away for the weekend in Norfolk. Of course, if you'd given me more notice . . . ' He replaced the diary in his right hand desk drawer and picked up his cigar once more.

'It wasn't possible,' I said. 'It was the only weekend the Council could manage.'

'Mmmm,' he murmured, as he began, once again, to read the letter he'd been looking at when I'd arrived.

'Of course,' I continued, 'we still need a pictures man.'

'Really?' he said, still studying his correspondence.

'Yes, as much for the valuation of Carforth House as for the free valuation days.'

'Are you certain you can't handle it? It's a long trek for some minor collection of second rate nineteenth century daubs, you know.'

'I think we should be safe rather than sorry, Charles,' I persisted. 'There may turn out to be some reasonable pictures there.'

'But even if there are,' he said, looking up, 'the Council's not going to sell them, is it?'

'No, of course not. Carforth House is a straightforward insurance valuation, but you never know what the public might bring in on the valuation days.'

He smiled condescendingly. 'Well, my experience of valuation days would suggest that you needn't bother to hire armed security guards.'

'I must have a pictures specialist,' I insisted.

'I'll see if Hugh Archibald's prepared to spare you a day,' he said, picking up another letter.

'I'll need him from the Thursday through to the Sunday.'

'Impossible.'

'I shall expect him to be there,' I said, quietly but firmly. Then, without waiting for a reply, I turned and left the Director of Pictures' office.

Back at my own desk I sat and looked through the Carforth House file. It looked as though it would all hang together, but only just.

'Have you got a team yet?' Charlotte asked.

'Just about,' I replied. 'Two for ceramics, one for furniture for the valuation itself but not for the weekend, one for silver, hopefully one for pictures, Bob Derby and myself.'

'Should be enough, shouldn't it?'

'I don't know. I've never arranged a valuation weekend before. And I'm getting very mixed signals. Bob Derby and Bernard Thornton seem to think there could be quite a good attendance, whereas Morrison-Whyte and Faulkner are so uninterested they're both pleading prior engagements.'

'Well, what do you expect from those two?'

'I know – but what if they're right?' I said. 'What if they're right?'

It had appeared to be perfectly simple when I'd devised the plan, but now it was far less cut and dried. A potential for real disaster seemed to be creeping in.

It had all started with a letter from the Clerk of Buttley Council asking if Hampson's would be interested in tendering for an insurance valuation of the contents of Carforth House, a sizeable seventeenth century mansion that now fell within the Council's remit. The Clerk had made it clear that he was approaching all leading auctioneers, and that the Council was operating on a very tight budget.

I wrote back to him the following day with a suggestion which even Charlotte agreed was inspired: I offered to undertake the valuation for a fee which would just about cover our expenses, on condition that the Council permitted us to use Carforth House for a valuation weekend. Although this sort of 'Roadshow' is now common, it wasn't then. The opportunities for members of the public to have appraisals free of charge on their own doorsteps came few and far between.

The good burghers of Buttley recognised a bargain when they saw one and promptly accepted my offer. With their acceptance arose the first problem; the only available date was in just four weeks time. That did not leave a lot of time for preparation and publicity, and due to another valuation commitment, I wouldn't be able to travel up to Buttley until the Friday evening.

'What if Hugh Archibald can't make it?' I said to Charlotte.

'He will.'

'And if we don't get a decent attendance . . .'

'You will.'

'But if we don't, and we don't get anything worthwhile for sale . . .'

'You will,' Charlotte reassured me. 'You worry too much. I'm sure you'll have queues of people. After all, it's going to be advertised in the local newspapers, isn't it?'

Chapter 20

By a quarter to ten the queue was already winding back from the closed doors of Carforth House, down the wide, stone steps and across the gravel drive. From there it stretched back along the tarmac path, eventually disappearing through the ancient yew hedge into the car park. There must have been six or seven hundred people there and we still had another fifteen minutes to go before we were officially due to open the doors.

'I've never seen anything like it,' Bob Derby remarked, as we gazed out on the crocodile of humanity from the safety of a first-floor window. 'And all due to five minutes' television coverage.'

'I can't think of anything else to attribute it to,' I said. 'I certainly don't think we can put it down to our advertising campaign in the local papers.'

'You can say that again,' he replied, and whistled through his teeth.

I had arrived at the Carforth Arms Hotel late on the previous evening. Two members of the valuation team had already gone to their beds, but Philip Lawrence and Hugh Archibald were keeping the barman company.

Hugh was a normally quiet-spoken, rather serious chap in his early twenties who was an extremely valuable right-hand man to Charles Morrison-Whyte. Despite a self-effacing nature he had already demonstrated to me on more than one occasion an extensive knowledge of his wide subject. So much so, that I tended to deal with him rather than his boss. It was usually less arduous.

'You two look happy,' I said, as I collapsed into a large easy chair at their table.

'Of course,' Hugh said, grinning broadly. 'We're stars. Haven't you heard?'

'I'd always suspected as much,' I replied, loosening my tie as the barman arrived with a large Scotch. 'Although, I'd looked upon you as artistes rather than stars, I suppose.'

'Cut the sarcasm, Harton,' Philip said, sprawling expansively in his chair. 'While you were swanning around the metropolis today, we were up here, not only doing your valuation for you but also making Hampson's a household name in North Yorkshire.'

'Oh, no! You haven't been going around knocking again?'

'I shall ignore that feeble attempt to link us with the lowest form of antique dealing life,' he continued. 'We – and when I say we, I mean the entire Hampson's team currently billeted in this less than luxurious establishment – have featured on . . .'

'Television!' Hugh Archibald interrupted. 'We've been on television – publicising the valuation weekend.'

'What . . .!'

'You may well sit there open-mouthed, Richard,' Philip went on. 'We got nearly ten minutes of prime time local television this evening. I wouldn't be surprised if all over North Yorkshire at this very moment . . .'

'Carrier bags packed with bric-à-brac,' Hugh cut in, 'and boxes of indescribable junk are being loaded into everything from station wagons to bicycle paniers . . .'

'All right! All right! Don't go mad,' Philip said. Then he turned to me. 'Do you remember that nice, quiet, young chap who used to work in the Pictures Department?'

'Hugh Archibald, you mean?'

272

'That's the boy – wouldn't say boo to a goose. Then, one day . . .'

'Fame!' I said.

'Glamour!' he went on.

'The bright lights!' I added.

'Oh, shut up you two,' said our victim as he sank lower in his chair. 'You've got to admit, it's pretty good that we got on the box.'

'Miraculous,' I agreed. 'But how did it happen?'

'With classic simplicity,' Philip explained. 'The local magazine programme lost a story at the last moment and needed to fill the gap. One of their researchers had seen our advertisement in his local paper – Hey Presto! Bingo!'

'Just like that?'

'Just like that. They telephoned us here this morning and sent round the camera crew this afternoon.'

'Brilliant,' I said. 'What did the Council have to say about it?'

'No idea. I'm not even sure they knew it was happening. Why?'

'Oh, nothing really. It's just that I suppose somebody should have asked their permission to film.'

'Well, I think the film crew would have done that,' Philip said.

'Oh, I should think so,' Hugh confirmed.

'Yes,' I agreed, 'I expect you're right.'

'Bloody hell!' Bernard Thornton commented when he joined Bob Derby and me at the first-floor window. 'I've never seen so many punters. Look at all those carrier bags and boxes.'

'I shudder to think what they've got in them,' I said.

'Makes me feel sick just to think of it,' Bernard remarked. 'And talking of feeling below par, how are you this morning?'

His question was addressed to Philip Lawrence who had just joined us.

'Nothing wrong with me, Bernard, I can assure you
. . . My God! Look at that lot!'

'Okay, fellas,' Bob Derby said, turning away from the
window. 'Action stations! It's time to get those doors
open. Everyone to his appropriate room. Richard, you
and I can vet the people as they come in and direct them
to the appropriate specialist.'

'Vet and direct!' Philip muttered, disparagingly, as
the chairman made for the stairs. 'Good to see you two
latecomers are going to continue leading from behind.'

Our initial plan had allowed for the entrance hall to
be a kind of sorting area where Bob and I would
discover what the people had and then decide whether
it was worth referring them to a specialist. In the corner
of the hall we'd set up a little display which told the story
of Hampson's and explained all about the wonderful
service we could provide. The idea being that it would
both entertain and inform the public as they waited. On
top of that there was a loop-tape of extremely tasteful
background music, chiefly Mozart piano pieces, which
Bob Derby felt would be nice and relaxing if the going
got tough. Each playing lasted twelve minutes exactly.

The opening chords of the Mozart were just
beginning to echo through the otherwise still, calm
building when Bob Derby drew back the bolts on the
massive front doors.

'Good Morning, ladies and gentle . . .'

Powerfully built though he was, the initial surge of
people momentarily picked him up and tossed him
backwards into the centre of the hall. Like an avenging
barbarian horde, bristling with furniture, boxes,
shopping bags, standard lamps and several unpleasant
looking examples of edged weaponry, they burst into
the formerly civilised surroundings of Carforth House.
The only question was whether to stand one's ground or
to just accept the inevitability of a rout and turn and
run.

'Ladies and gentlemen!' Hampson's chairman bellowed from somewhere in the middle of the throng. 'If I could just ask you to be patient for a little while longer, we'll deal with you just as quickly as we can.'

'Excuse me . . . excuse me . . . excuse me . . . ' I called, as I formed an emergency barricade with an old oak refectory table which had been standing against one wall.

As I leapt behind the table, the crowd ebbed and flowed violently as the shock waves produced by the sudden, initial surge and the equally abrupt halt, worked their way back down the queue to the car park. Bob Derby and I quickly dragged a second table into line with the first, completing our redoubt, then we paused for a moment to get our breath.

'Good God!' he muttered, 'I wasn't expecting that.'

'Nor was I,' I replied.

'Well, I suppose we'd better get started,' he said, turning to face the mob. 'Right! Ladies and gentlemen! Who is first?'

The idea was that he and I should screen everything being brought in, give on the spot appraisals of the junk and refer anything decent to the appropriate specialists. In theory it was fine. Unfortunately, in practice, there were just too many of them and too few of us. If every single item was unwrapped for inspection, then re-wrapped again prior to the owner either taking it to the specialist or just taking it away, the delay caused would be immense. Even with the two of us dealing with up to half a dozen people each at any one time, we could still hear the natives getting restless.

'This is noo good . . . it'll tak' hours . . . ah don't think they know what they're doin' . . . ooh, ah wouldn't 'ave cum if ah'd knowed 'twere goin' to be like this . . . well I think it's a jolly poor show . . .'

The only immediate solution seemed to be to open the floodgates and let a group of them through to the

275

currently under-employed specialists elsewhere in the house.

'And you have . . . ?' I enquired of an elderly lady whose grey head was crowned with the sort of hat I'd last seen circa 1956.

'Oh . . . well . . . dear me . . . well, I have some silver . . .'

'Straight through that door there,' I said, pointing to Philip Lawrence's temporary home.

'Oh . . . well . . . I'm not sure . . . that is . . .'

'That's all right,' I insisted, taking her by the arm and gently propelling her towards the door. 'Mr Lawrence will be pleased to discuss it with you.'

Looking a little bewildered but offering no further resistance, the old lady toddled off in the direction indicated.

'Now, who's next?' I asked.

'Ah reckon ah am,' volunteered a round, red-faced man. 'Least, ah've bin waitin' long enough.'

'What is it you've got, sir?'

'Ah don't know, tha's why ah've brought it in,' he said, placing a large newspaper-filled cardboard box on the table in front of me. 'If ah'd knowed what it was then ah'd not 'av bothered to stand in that bloody queue for the last two hours.'

There were a few giggles and a general murmur of agreement from the crowd behind him.

'Well, let's have a look at it, shall we?' I said brightly.

'That's what it's 'ere for,' the red-faced man confirmed, pushing the scruffy-looking box across the table towards me.

I opened it up, removed the top layer of newspaper and took out a dirty, rusting, rectangular canister with a small, round cap at the top. A few traces of paint remained on the thing.

'Well,' the man said, almost immediately, 'what d'you make of it?'

'It's a tea tin,' I said.

276

'A what?'

'A tea tin.'

'A bit bloody big for that in't it,' he said, sceptically.

'No, not really,' I assured him. 'They're not particularly rare.'

''Ow old is it then?'

'It dates from about 1900.'

'What'sit worth?'

Suddenly a dozen heads were craned forward, as the front couple of rows in the crowd behind him struggled to see and hear.

'Very little, I'm afraid,' I said, replacing the tea tin in the cardboard box, 'especially in this condition.'

''Ow little?'

'Very little – it effectively has no sale value at all.'

'None at all?' he sounded incredulous.

'Not really,' I confirmed. 'If it were in perfect condition, then there are collectors for this sort of domestic ephemera . . .'

'Kitchenalia.'

'Sorry?'

'Kitchenalia,' the redfaced man repeated. 'Tha's whatit's called – Kitchenalia.'

'Really?' I said, wondering why he'd bothered to bring it into us if he knew so much about it.

'Aye. Ah would've thought you would 'ave knowed that.'

'Well, it just goes to show,' I said, pushing the box back across the table towards him.

'Will you sell it?' he asked.

'I'm afraid not,' I replied, still measuring my tone carefully and managing to smile. 'As I mentioned – it's of no sale value in this condition.'

'Well, young man wha' would you say if ah told you ah'd bin offered twenty pounds for it?'

'I'd say rush back to whoever it was and accept the offer immediately.'

The redfaced man gave me a long, contemptuous look, picked up his cardboard box and turned to go.

'You're all wastin' your bloody time with 'im,' he advised the crowd as he started to make his way towards the door. 'Either 'e knows sod all or 'e's a bloody crook!'

'Now, who was next?' I said, as all the heads that had turned to follow the redfaced man's departure turned back again to look at me, the object of his abuse.

'Me, I think,' said a pukka-looking military type in sports jacket and cavalry twills.

'Right, sir, what have you got?'

'China, mainly,' he said.

'Fine. If you'd like to take it straight upstairs, you'll find the ceramics valuers in the first room on the right. I'm sure they'll be able to help you.'

'Thank you so much.'

'And the next.'

'I've got some old silver,' said a young lad.

'Okay, straight through to the silver specialist over there. Next . . .'

Despite the temporary hiccup caused by the redfaced man, the rapid dispersal of the throng in the entrance hall to the various specialists seemed to work fairly well. It's true that it reduced the role of Bob Derby and myself to that of little more than traffic policemen, but it certainly kept the crowd moving. At least, it kept moving into the specialists' rooms. I hadn't noticed that it was one way only and that nobody seemed to be returning.

'For Chrissake, Richard! What do you and our beloved chairman think you're doing?' hissed a voice behind me.

I turned to be confronted by an obviously over-excited Philip Lawrence. He was clutching a piece of lustre pottery.

'Why, what's the problem?'

'I can't bloody move in my room for people – that's what the problem is.'

'Oh.'

278

'And the faster I try and get rid of them the faster you're sending them through.'

'All right, we'll deal with more of them out here,' I said, looking through the window at the queue as it continued to trail back through the yew hedge to the car park. 'We were just trying to avoid a riot.'

'And it would speed things up if you didn't send me ceramics,' he added, holding up the silver lustre tea cup he was carrying.'

'Where did that come from?' I asked.

'It belongs to some old dear with a hat straight out of Bill and Ben the Flowerpot Men. She assured me that the nice man in the hall told her she should see the silver expert.'

'I remember her,' I sighed. 'But if I'd waited for her to get round to telling me what she'd actually got, we'd still be discussing it now.'

'I know,' Philip replied. 'Why do you think I've escaped out here.'

'Are you two going to stand there gassing all morning?' a rather florid Bob Derby called over.

'Tactical team-talk, Bob,' Philip replied. 'You keep going – you're doing brilliantly.'

Derby looked heavenwards and mouthed something inaudible.

'Good to see the skipper's enjoying himself,' Philip said, as he headed back to his room. 'And do try to hold the buggers back for a while, Richard.'

'I'll try,' I said, and returned to my table. 'Sorry to have kept you waiting – who's next?'

'Ah reckon it's us,' replied a solidly square man with a brush of close cropped grey hair and a pair of National Health glasses bound with pink sticky tape. His nose and cheeks were a filigree of tiny red and blue veins while the eyes behind the glasses were a cold ice-blue.

'Aye, ah should say so,' concurred the lady next to him. 'Go on, show 'im, Arthur, and let's be gone. Ah've

279

not done the shoppin' yet.' She pushed him forward to the table and glared at me defiantly as though she expected an argument.

Nothing was further from my mind. She was roughly the same build as her companion but seemed a lot more aggressive.

'How can I help you?' I asked in my oiliest Belgravia voice.

'You can tell us what that's worth,' said Arthur, thrusting a long thin package into my hand.

I folded back the brown paper wrapping and took out a silver marrow spoon.

'This is nice,' I said. 'It's a . . .'

'We know what it is,' interrupted the woman.

'Aye,' agreed Arthur, 'it's a cheese scoop.'

'Actually, it's not,' I corrected him, 'it's a marrow spoon.'

'A marra spoon!' the woman said, with a snort of derision. 'How can it be a marra spoon?'

'Aye,' agreed Arthur, 'what good would somethin' as small as that be for a marra? I suppose it might be all right for them corvettes what they grow now, but it'd be no good at all for a marra, no good at all.'

The crowd muttered and nodded in general agreement. It was obvious to them that I knew less about horticulture than I did about antique silver, and by then they were pretty certain I didn't know much about that either.

'No, no,' I persevered, 'it's got nothing to do with vegetable marrows. It was for removing the marrow from bones. That's why it looks so much like a cheese scoop, with these long, narrow bowls at either end of the handle.'

The man and woman looked first at the marrow spoon, then at me. Although each look conveyed deep-seated doubt, they said nothing.

'They were first made during the reign of Queen

Anne,' I went on, 'but this one is George II, I think. I breathed on the hallmarks to make them more easily readable. 'Yes,' I confirmed, 'it's London, 1748, maker's mark – PG. I think that's Phillips Garden, but I'd have to check it up.'

Suddenly there was something approaching respect in the eyes of Arthur and his lady. What was more, the mob had gone silent. They were hanging on my every word.

'On the other hand, you can take it through to our silver specialist . . .'

'No, no, ah reckon you knows what you're talkin' abat,' Arthur said. 'What's it worth then?'

'Well, they are collected,' I replied. 'I would expect it to make a hundred and fifty to two hundred pounds under the hammer.'

'Sell it!' boomed Arthur's companion without a moment's hesitation.

'Aye,' Arthur concurred. 'Can you do that for us?'

'We'd be delighted to.'

'Go on then lad – it's no good to us. We're not likely to be buyin' any marrabones.'

A few minutes later, Mr and Mrs Arthur Fenley, equipped with a Hampson's receipt for their marrow spoon, fought their way out of Carforth House to go about their shopping. I breathed a sigh of relief. Getting the first item in for sale was always rather like breaking your duck at the wicket.

'Sorry to have kept you waiting ladies and gentlemen,' I said. 'Who is next? . . . yes, madam, what can I do for you?'

At five o'clock precisely, two sounds broke the pristine silence in the entrance hall of Carforth House. The first was the crash of Bob Derby closing the front doors, the second was the particularly tasteful piece of Mozart starting up for something like the thirtieth time that day.

'Ahhh! I can't stand it!' I howled.

'Turn it off! Turn it off!' Derby bawled. 'For God's

281

sake, turn the bloody thing off before it drives me mad!'

I flipped the mains switch and suddenly all that could be heard was the twittering of the birds outside, and the ticking of the old longcase clock at the foot of the stairs.

'Hell!' he said, as he staggered over to the nearest chair and collapsed onto it. 'I don't think I've ever spoken to so many people in one day.'

'Or seen so much junk,' I added.

'No, you're right there. Mind you, there was a lot of good stuff as well, not that I've any idea how much of it's been left for sale.'

'A fair amount, I think,' I said.

At that moment, Bernard Thornton's face peered over the heavy oak bannister rail above us. He looked onto the now all but deserted hall. Then he spoke, his voice percolating down in an eerie, ghostlike whisper. 'Have they gone?' he said.

'Yes, Bernard,' Bob Derby replied, 'it's safe. You can come down now.'

Followed close behind by an exhausted-looking William Baron, Bernard Thornton trudged noisily down the old, creaking staircase. His arms hung loose at his sides, his bow-tie looked even more like a crushed butterfly than usual, and his shirt sleeves were undone at the cuffs. It was obvious from these and a few other outward signs that Bernard Thornton had had a hard day.

'I thought they'd never stop coming,' he said. 'Every time I looked up, there seemed to be more and more of them. I seriously considered jumping from our window at one stage.'

'Have you taken anything decent for sale?' Bob Derby asked. 'That's the bottom line.'

Bernard Thornton looked pained. 'The bottom what?' he enquired.

'The bottom line, Bernard. You know quite well what I mean.'

282

'I presume you mean that's what will determine whether this venture is profitable or not.'

'Yes, Bernard, that more or less sums it up.'

'Then I don't understand why you don't just say so, without resort to vulgar Americanisms, Robert. After all, if I'd wished to be addressed like a New York certified accountant, I would have become a New York certified accountant.'

'That profession's loss is auctioneering's gain, Bernard,' Bob replied, patiently. 'But, now, if you can recall my original question . . .'

Bernard Thornton, who by then was settling himself into one of the window seats, looked blank for a moment. 'Your original question? Oh, yes – did we take in anything decent . . . yes . . . I'm sure we did . . . didn't we, William?' He looked across innocently to his assistant who had seated himself on the second tread of the staircase. 'What *did* we take in, William? You did all the paperwork. It's all a blur to me.'

'Nothing wildly outstanding,' he replied, 'but a lot of good bread and butter stuff – several nice, large pieces of Chinese Export, a good Worcester dessert service, that sort of thing.'

'Good,' Derby said. 'How about pictures? Where's Hugh? Anybody seen him?'

'When I stuck my head into his room about ten minutes ago,' William said, 'he was sitting bolt upright behind his table with a fixed smile on his face. I think he may be dead.'

'Fine, fine. How about Philip? Where's he?'

'Here!' shouted a voice from the silver room, 'and unless one of you lot helps me to finish the paperwork on this stuff, this is where I shall remain for some time to come.'

'All right,' I called, dragging myself to my feet, 'I'm coming.'

'The amazing thought is,' Bernard remarked, 'that

we've got another day of the same tomorrow.'

'Oh, I don't think we'll be looking at the same sort of numbers tomorrow,' Bob replied. 'I think they all came today. The only ones we'll see tomorrow are those who weren't prepared to stand in that queue today. No, I'll lay you ten to one we'll be back to normal tomorrow.'

The old trees in what little remained of the parkland that had once surrounded Carforth House looked particularly dramatic against the dark, spring storm clouds. As each purple-black cumulus raced away, bright splashes of sunlight temporarily illuminated the house and grounds. Then the next shadows would once more envelope everything in gloom.

'Amazing,' remarked Bernard Thornton.

'Incredible,' agreed Bob Derby.

But neither of them was referring to the Turneresque sky or landscape. It was the awesome queue that, by a quarter past nine on Sunday morning, already stretched from Carforth House back through the yew hedge to the car park.

'I just don't know where they're all coming from,' I added. 'I didn't think there were this many people in Yorkshire.'

'I want to go home,' Philip groaned. 'I didn't join up for this. I just wanted to have fun and see the world. I quit. I resign.'

'If I see one more overpainted print laid on glass, I will very probably join you,' Hugh Archibald contributed.

'I don't know what's wrong with you chaps,' Bob Derby said, still gazing out at the column of raincoats and hats below us. 'Look at all that business down there. Just think of those fat departmental bonuses.'

'Though it pains me to do so,' Philip replied, 'I think I should remind you that a considerable percentage of my last quarter's fat departmental bonus is now in your wallet, Mr Derby.'

284

'Yes,' the Chairman acknowledged with a cheerful smile, 'you did have a wretched run of cards last night, didn't you?'

'Yes, didn't I.'

'Never mind! All the more reason to get started on that lot down there and give your next bonus a boost.'

'I can't wait,' came the sour reply.

'Okay then, chaps,' Bob went on, as he made for the stairs, 'we may as well open up early and make them happy. I think it'll be smoother today – we'd got the system going just about right by yesterday afternoon. Oh, and one other thing . . .'

'What's that?'

'The first person to turn that blasted music on is fired!'

Bob Derby was right about the system having sorted itself out. All morning and most of the afternoon we worked our way slowly but steadily through the seemingly endless train of people. They, in turn, remained generally bright and patient despite the periodic heavy showers which swept the grounds. Each time the heavens opened, hundreds of umbrellas bloomed above the waiting throng only to disappear again with the first rays of the returning sun. All in all, I was very happy with the way things were going. Happy, that is, until I noticed a familiar red face in the press of people just outside the door. My friend with the kitchenalia was back.

As soon as I spotted him, and despite the general clamour, I began to pick up snatches of his conversation.

' . . . waste of time really . . . 'e knows nothing . . . twenty pounds, cash . . . they won't be told . . . they think we're all daft up 'ere cos we don't talk all hoity-toity . . .'

I was well used to his sort but I did secretly hope that he would end up annoying Bob Derby this time rather than me. Not that there was really any chance of that. It was me he was after, and if that meant waiting a little bit longer, then he was prepared to wait. After all, there was a captive audience to address.

'. . . ah mean, it's not as though this lot's first division . . . they all know me at Christie's of course . . . we must admit it, Mr Cawthorne, you wus right an' we wus wrong . . . well, when all's said an' dun, they're your proper aristocracy, not like this loada cowboys . . .'

'Can I help you, sir?' I interrupted.

'Ah don't know, lad. That depends.'

'On what, sir?'

'On whether you know owt or nowt about china.'

'Well, why don't I have a look and then you can make up your own mind on that,' I said, mustering as blithe a smile as I could manage.

He, in turn, bared a set of tiny, sharply-pointed yellow teeth in an unpleasant smirk, and pushed a cardboard box across the table towards me.

'There y'are then, mister,' he said. 'Tell me what you know about that lot.'

One by one, I unwrapped the contents of the box, and with each additional piece my heart soared with joy. I didn't care what Mr Cawthorne thought this particular lot was – I knew.

'How long have you had these?' I asked.

'Years.'

'How many years?'

'What's this then? Twenty questions?'

'No, I was just curious.'

'Oh, just curious? Ah see,' he said, smiling malevolently. 'Well, for your information, they was my aunty's, an' she were eighty-two when she died – God rest her soul.'

It always struck me as curious how people tended to offer the age at death of the previous owner as a guarantee of the age and authenticity of a piece. For all

I knew, Aunty – God rest her soul – might have died the day before yesterday and only bought the things the day before that. If that were so, the items on the table in front of me might only be a week old.

'Interesting,' I observed.

The red-faced man made no reply.

'Because, these items are no more than a year or so old at the most.'

'You what . . .?'

'These pieces are modern – made within the last few years.'

'Don't talk such damned rubbish, man,' he spluttered, his red face deepening several shades. 'Ah've told yer: they was me aunty's!'

'I can't help that, sir. These figures are fakes.'

'Yer off yer 'ead, man! You don't know nothin'!' He turned to the intrigued crowd which, having scented blood, had gathered around our table: 'Ah said, didn't ah – 'e knows nothin'!'

'If you would prefer to show these pieces to one of our ceramics specialists,' I went on, 'please feel free to do so. But I'm absolutely certain they'll simply confirm what I've just told you.'

'Ah don't doubt it,' he snapped, his colour deeper than ever, as he unceremoniously swept the things back into their box. 'You're all in it together. You're all bloody crooks!' And with that, he picked up his cardboard box, and barged his way through the crowd and out of Carforth House, shouting abuse as he went.

'What was that all about?' Bob Derby asked.

'A collection of fake Staffordshire figures,' I said.

'Oh, is that all. The fuss he was making I thought it was the Crown Jewels at the very least.'

I shook my head and smiled. 'Who's next?' I asked turning back to the crowd around my table.

'Me, I think,' said a middle-aged man who'd witnessed the whole débâcle.

'Fine. What have you got, sir?'

As he unpacked some nice nineteenth century bronzes, he plucked up the courage to ask about the red-faced man.

'How could you be so sure that his figures were fakes?'

'Well, there are a lot of them about now,' I said, 'and there are several giveaway signs.'

'But they looked so old,' he said.

'That's one of the giveaway signs. I don't know if you noticed, but the whole surface of the glaze was covered in tiny, dirty-looking cracks.'

'Yes, I saw that.'

'Well, the fakers achieve that crazing by dunking the figures into a cold, dark liquid while they're still hot – I understand coffee works quite well. The glaze crazes immediately and discolours at the same time. It's quite convincing until you compare it with an original, because then you'll see that the network of cracks is much too tight and regular.'

'Well, I never!'

'Anyway, you've got nothing to worry about. These are rather nice bronzes. Have they been in your family long?'

'As a matter of fact, yes, they have. I inherited them from my father, and he was nearly ninety when he died . . .'

It wasn't until nearly twenty minutes past five that the last customers made their way back to their cars. None of us had any idea how many people we'd seen over the two days, but it was certainly several thousand. Now it was over, and Carforth House was once again quiet enough to hear the ticking of the old longcase clock at the foot of the stairs.

This time we hadn't bothered to close and bolt the front door. The weather had cleared and the wind had dropped, leaving us with a gloriously sunny, late spring evening which I was taking in from where I sat. Framed by the doorway, the view appeared to be a rolling panorama of uninterrupted parkland. It was an optical illusion of course. Just out of frame, the architectural horrors of post-war Buttley gnawed at the fringes of all that was left of the park. It didn't matter; for a few moments one could dream.

Reality intervened in the form of a substantial, silhouetted figure which materialised suddenly, obliterating both landscape and fantasy.

'I'm sorry,' I said, screwing up my eyes in an effort to identify some distinguishing features of the shadow, 'but we closed officially at five o'clock.'

'And not before time!' the figure boomed in an impressive basso-profundo that echoed around the hall. 'I want to see Mr Harton – immediately!'

Something told me that the visitor didn't want me to inspect his collection of petit point antimacassars or his cased arrangement of rare butterflies.

I rose to my feet, glancing around to see if anybody else was at hand. Naturally, for the first time in two days, I was on my own.

'I'm Richard Harton,' I said. 'How can I help you?'

'Well, if you had a garden fork or spade with you, I'd suggest you got down to the rose garden right away and started sorting it out.'

'What?'

'The rose garden! Down by the car park – have you not seen it?'

'Yes, I've seen it. In fact I've remarked to my colleagues how delightful it is . . .'

'Was, Mr Harton! Was!' thundered the silhouette.

'I don't understand.'

'Nor do I! I don't understand how you could let thousands of people run riot in such a way. I do not understand how you could do it!'

'I'm sorry,' I said, 'but I really have no idea what

289

you're talking about, sir. Or, for that matter, who you are.'

'I am talking about the desecration of Buttley's municipal rose garden, Mr Harton. And, for your information, I am Councillor Gausden, Mayor of Buttley.'

So saying, he stepped out of the doorway into the body of the hall, and became properly visible for the first time.

The Mayor of Buttley was a big man with a full head of thick black hair which probably made him look a little younger than he was. He was a good two stone overweight, however, and the waistcoat of his sober, charcoal-grey suit seemed to be in imminent danger of parting company with its buttons as it struggled to contain the mayor's own personal corporation. With the twin exceptions that he wore neither a gold watch chain nor brown boots, I felt he was otherwise every inch what a mayor should be. Nevertheless, I still had no idea what he was talking about.

'I'm sorry, Mr Gausden, but I don't understand what the rose gardens have got to do with Hampson's,' I said.

'Then you follow me, Mr Harton, and I'll soon show you.'

On arrival at Buttley's municipal rose gardens I could see what he meant. Although the actual beds and their contents were intact, the grass did look rather the worse for wear.

The gardens had obviously served as a playground for considerable numbers of bored little darlings while mummies and daddies had shuffled ever onward in the interminable queue. The combination of lots of little feet and a fair number of heavy showers had reduced some of the immaculately manicured paths to muddy tracks.

'Do you see that, Mr Harton?' Mayor Gausden asked, indicating the full extent of the damage with a broad sweep of his right arm. 'Do you see that?'

'Yes, Mr Mayor,' I replied solemnly. 'It's a bit of a mess, isn't it.'

290

'A bit of a mess!' he exclaimed. 'I can assure you that it's a lot more serious than that. I can tell you now, the Amenities Committee will not be amused when this is brought to their attention.'

His tone of voice made it clear that public trial at Nuremburg carried less of a stigma than being arraigned before the Amenities Committee of Buttley Council.

'Whilst not wishing to accept any responsibility for what has happened here,' I began carefully, 'I'm sure that Hampson's would not wish the Council to be out of pocket as a result of our valuation weekend – no matter how indirect the link might be.'

'Taken as read, Mr Harton,' replied the Mayor, with a note of cautious optimism.

'I wonder, therefore,' I continued, 'if we might make a small donation towards the Amenities Committee's funds?'

'I'm sure such a gesture would be greatly appreciated, Mr Harton.' He moved closer and looked very serious. 'Had you any particular figure in mind?'

'Well, as you probably know, we're only charging a nominal fee for this valuation . . .'

'I did hear as much.'

'But I'm sure we could reduce it by a further . . . say . . . forty pounds?'

There was a sharp intake of breath. 'I reckon the grass seed alone could set us back twenty,' he said, shaking his head sorrowfully. 'And, of course, our permission was not sought for filming – another serious matter . . .'

'Really? I had no idea! What if we said sixty?'

He suddenly grasped my right hand in a grip that would have reduced granite to dust. 'Sixty it is, Mr Harton,' he confirmed, as confidentially as his overdeveloped larynx would permit. 'And may I say, what a kind gesture it is.'

'Please don't mention it, Mr Mayor,' I said, wresting my crushed hand from his, 'it's the least we can do.'

Although everybody else headed back to London that evening, I stayed on in Buttley. Quite a few people with furniture too large to transport to Carforth House had called us, and I was going to spend the following morning on calls. It would be nice if one of the appointments turned out to be fruitful, but even if they were all run of the mill, one thing was already certain: the weekend had been a success.

Chapter 21

It was almost five o'clock when I arrived back at Vanbrugh Street the following afternoon. Charlotte was hard at work.

'Hi!' she said, 'I understand the weekend was a great success.'

'If sheer numbers of people are anything to go by – yes, I would say it was. Any messages for me?'

'Yes, there're half a dozen on your desk but none of them are urgent.'

'Okay.'

'And Bob Derby wants you to call him. It must be good – he called me Sweetheart.'

'Oh, dear! That's to be discouraged.'

'You can say that again,' she said, as she leafed through the notes on her desk. 'And Sarah called to say she'd missed you over the weekend – isn't that nice? . . .'

'Isn't it,' I agreed.

' . . . and unless she hears to the contrary she'll expect you at her place at eight then she'll treat you to dinner à deux at the local bistro . . .'

'Fine.'

' . . . and an Antonia Cartwright called. Apparently she's in London for just one night, staying at Brown's. She'd just love to see you if you're free – which, of course, you're not. But if you were you could call her at Brown's before seven. She said she'd understand if she didn't hear from you. Okay? . . . Richard? . . . okay? . . . earth to Mr Harton – come in, please.'

'What? . . . oh . . . sorry . . . what did you say?'

'How far would you like me to go back – supper à deux with Sarah or Brown's hotel?'

She didn't have to repeat any of it. I'd heard every word. Just the mention of Antonia's name had taken me back ten months in an instant, but I'd heard every word.

'Was Antonia your grande amour in Sussex?' Charlotte asked, after a while.

I nodded.

'I thought so,' she said. 'What are you going to do?'

'I honestly don't know,' I replied.

In silence she tidied the top of her desk, then walked over and collected her things from the cupboard just inside the door.

'I know it's none of my business, Richard,' she said, as she slipped her raincoat on, 'but I hope things sort themselves out tonight – one way or the other.'

'I expect they will.'

'Yes,' she said, as she opened the office door, 'I expect they will – and don't forget to call Bob Derby.'

'I won't,' I said.

I listened to her footsteps going down the stairs and waited for the street door to slam before I reached for the telephone.

'You look a bit tired.'

'I am a bit,' I said.

'I suppose it's this whizz-kid executive life you live now.'

'Two and a half days in Yorkshire does not constitute living the life of a whizz-kid,' I said, taking another sip from my port.

'No, but it's a lot different to what you were doing before you joined Hampson's isn't it?'

'Oh, sure,' I agreed. 'In fact, it's funny you should

mention that. I spoke to my Chairman this afternoon when I got back: my four month's trial with Hampson's was up at the end of last month and we'd both forgotten about it.'

'What did he have to say?'

'He was very complimentary – I was lucky the valuation weekend was a success.'

'Pay rise?' she suggested.

'As it happens, yes,' I laughed. 'And the promise of taking smart sales at Hampson's.'

'The big time!'

'Sort of.'

'Do you have any regrets?'

'About what?'

'Oh, I don't know – leaving Sussex? . . .'

'No.'

'. . . coming to London? . . .'

'No.'

'. . . me? . . .'

I put my port down on the table, and reached out and took her hand. 'No, Sarah,' I said, 'especially no regrets about you.'

'Good morning, Charlotte. Isn't it a beautiful morning?'

She looked up a little suspiciously from her desk, then at the window and the unseasonably grey day outside. 'If you say so,' she said.

'I do,' I replied, helping myself to coffee.

She watched me in silence for some time, then couldn't contain herself any longer. 'Well! Where did you go last night – Brown's or the bistro?'

'The bistro of course. I had dinner with Sarah.'

'Oh,' she grinned. 'I am glad!'

'So am I,' I said.

'Never mind,' she went on, handing me a note, 'here's something that'll bring you back to earth.'

'What's this?'

295

'She wants an insurance valuation of some pictures in a hurry.'

'Mrs Lindt?' I read. 'Never heard of her.'

'No, she's not used us before.'

'This Highgate address rings a bell, though.'

'I thought it might. She was recommended to contact you by an old friend of hers who lives in the next block.'

I scratched my head. 'But I've only been on one valuation in Highgate, and that was . . . oh, no! . . .'

'Oh, yes.'

' . . . you mean . . .'

'I'm afraid so – Mrs Popkiewicz liked you so much, she's recommending you to her friends.'